Progress in SEPARATION AND PURIFICATION, Volume 2

MODERN SEPARATION METHODS OF MACROMOLECULES AND PARTICLES

A Wiley-Interscience Series

Progress in
SEPARATION AND PURIFICATION

SERIES EDITORS

E. S. Perry, Research Laboratories, Eastman Kodak Company,
Rochester, New York

C. J. van Oss, School of Medicine, State University of
New York at Buffalo, Buffalo, New York

This volume is based on a Symposium sponsored by the University of
Wisconsin Extension, the Department of Postgraduate Medical Education of
the University of Wisconsin Medical Center, and Beckman Instruments, Inc.,
and held at Madison, Wisconsin, on February 7-8, 1968.

Progress in Separation and Purification, Volume 2

MODERN SEPARATION METHODS OF MACROMOLECULES AND PARTICLES

EDITED BY

THEO GERRITSEN

Department of Pediatrics and Physiological Chemistry
University of Wisconsin Medical Center
Madison, Wisconsin

WILEY-INTERSCIENCE

A DIVISION OF JOHN WILEY & SONS
NEW YORK · LONDON · SYDNEY · TORONTO

Copyright © 1969 by John Wiley & Sons, Inc.

10 9 8 7 6 5 4 3 2 1

Library of Congress Catalog Card Number 69-14292
SBN 470 29695 X

Printed in the United States of America

Introduction to the Series

Through the ages man has been aware of the importance of separating the valuable from the less valuable in nature's mixtures. This trait has persisted; it is difficult to single out an area of science of a science-based industry where separations and purifications do not play an important role. Yet, in spite of this heritage, only within recent times has the science of separations been recognized in its individuality and has finally been accorded independent identity. The beginning of this era is difficult to pinpoint, but it is approximately the time of the second world war. Certainly, the science and technology generated in the struggle to separate the fissionable isotopes, to isolate and purify marketable quantities of antibiotics, the discovery of gas-phase chromatography, and the industries based on solid-state phenomena were important factors in leading the way for the science of separations and purifications as we know it today.

In the intervening twenty-five to thirty years, there has occurred an extensive development in this field. The literature has grown immensely; it is still expanding at a rapid rate for both the science and the technology of the subject, and a forum is needed for specialists as well as those new to the field or those working in related areas to keep up with the development. *Progress in Separation and Purification* is devoted to this purpose. Its broadest objective is to provide its readers with a high degree of current awareness on the progress being made in the large and complex field. We hope that the Series will help the practitioner to keep abreast of the ever growing literature by providing him with authoritative summaries on significant new developments and critical evaluations of new methods, apparatus, and techniques. The organization and condensation of the literature which is now dispersed throughout the chemical, biological, and nuclear sciences will also help to bring to the science and technology of separations its rightful status.

Fast and expeditious reporting are particular objectives of this Series. We plan to publish volumes at intervals commensurate with the procurement of articles. Manuscripts will be processed as received, and a volume will be issued when sufficient material has been assembled. The choice of subject and the manner in which ideas and opinions are expressed are essentially left to the discretion of the authors. Our only request of them is to render a service which will be of value to the reader and to the science and technology of separation and purification.

EDMOND S. PERRY
CAREL J. VAN OSS

Preface

The fast and extensive development in methodology and techniques which are available for the investigator in the biological field, is almost overwhelming.

After a successful Symposium in 1966, on the topic of "Modern Applications of Column Chromatography" (the proceedings of which were not published), the topic for the 1968 Meeting was decided to be concerned with different separation methods of macromolecules. Discussions with interested speakers in the United States and in Europe resulted in an extension of the field to "Macromolecules and Particles." An attempt was made to include in the program as many different approaches as possible: disc and free-flow electrophoresis, gradient centrifugation and resolubilization methods, partition and counter-current distribution, and agarose gel-filtration. Two different methods were discussed for the separation of lymphocyte populations, and a new approach to the separation of macromolecules, called "differential elution" was reported. That the program was successful may be exemplified by the fact that 650 people attended the Symposium while less than half that number was expected.

Although Professor Albertsson was unable to attend the Symposium, and the subject of "Partition in Polymer Two-Phase Systems" was presented by Drs. Walter and Pettijohn, Professor Albertsson, at our request, contributed to this volume with a report on recent work in the field performed in Sweden. For this I am very grateful.

Dr. Anderson's presentation on "Gradient Resolubilization Methods for Separating Macromolecules" is being published in the Quarterly Review of Biophysics (Cambridge University Press), and is therefore not included in this volume.

For the fact that the Proceedings of this Symposium are published as a volume in the Series *Progress in Separation and Purification,* I am most grateful to the editors of the Series and to the Publishers, and I am particularly indebted to all the contributors of this volume, for their splendid cooperation.

THEO GERRITSEN

March, 1969

Contributors

P.-Å. ALBERTSSON, *Department of Biochemistry, University of Umeå, Umeå, Sweden*

H-C. CHEN, *The Rockefeller University, New York City*

L. C. CRAIG, *The Rockefeller University, New York City*

M. H. EDGELL, *Division of Biology, California Institute of Technology, Pasadena, California*

K. HANNIG, *Max Planck Institut für Eiweiss und Lederforschung, Munich, Germany*

E. J. HARFENIST, *The Rockefeller University, New York City*

K. HELLSING, *Department of Medical Chemistry, University of Uppsala, Uppsala, Sweden*

C. A. HUTCHISON III, *Division of Biology, California Institute of Technology, Pasadena, California*

M. K. JOUSTRA, *Pharmacia Fine Chemicals AB, Uppsala, Sweden*

T. C. LAURENT, *Department of Medical Chemistry, University of Uppsala, Uppsala, Sweden*

B. ÖBRINK, *Department of Medical Chemistry, University of Uppsala, Uppsala, Sweden*

H. PERTOFT, *Department of Medical Chemistry, University of Uppsala, Uppsala, Sweden*

D. E. PETTIJOHN, *Department of Biophysics, University of Colorado Medical Center, Denver, Colorado*

K. SHORTMAN, *Walter and Eliza Hall Institute of Medical Research, Royal Melbourne Hospital, Melbourne, Victoria, Australia*

R. L. SINSHEIMER, *Division of Biology, California Institute of Technology, Pasadena, California*

O. SMITHIES, *Laboratory of Genetics, University of Wisconsin, Madison, Wisconsin*

M. SUNG, *Laboratory of Genetics, University of Wisconsin, Madison, Wisconsin*

H. WALTER, *Laboratory of Chemical Biology, Veterans Administration Hospital, Long Beach, and the Department of Biological Chemistry, UCLA School of Medicine, Los Angeles, California*

Å. WASTESON, *Department of Medical Chemistry, University of Uppsala, Uppsala, Sweden*

Contents

Large Pore "Disc" Electrophoresis

Marshall Hall Edgell, Clyde A. Hutchison III, and Robert L. Sinsheimer

Division of Biology, California Institute of Technology, Pasadena, California

I. INTRODUCTION

Polyacrylamide offers several advantages as a support material for electrophoretic separations. The polymerized gel is chemically inert and transparent to ultraviolet light. The gel is easy to handle and may be easily processed to locate the material being fractionated. Perhaps the most useful feature is the wide range of gel concentrations possible with polyacrylamide. Gels ranging from 2.5 to 30% polyacrylamide (by weight) have been successfully employed. The gel serves not only as an anticonvectant but also as a molecular sieve. Fractionation may occur both by size and by charge. Electrophoresis of proteins in polyacrylamide gel has become quite common since the introduction of the technique by Raymond and Weintraub (1) and Ornstein and Davis (2). The fractionation of peptides and nucleic acids in polyacrylamide is also becoming widespread. Electrophoresis of these macromolecules requires gel concentrations of 7% or greater to provide sieving. Particles made up of several molecular components may be electrophoresed by using more dilute gels. Tiselius has separated 30S and 50S ribosomal subunits in a 5% gel (3). We have been using 2.6% gels to electrophorese small bacteriophage (4). These phage consist of a

1

nucleic acid core and a coat composed of a large number of protein subunits.

II. PROCEDURE FOR DILUTE GELS

Our procedure is essentially that of Ornstein and Davis (2,5) modified for dilute gels. A diagrammatic representation of the various steps is shown in Figure 1. A 2.6% gel, 85% monomer, and 15% crosslinking agent, is polymerized in a 5-mm i.d. glass tube 6 cm long. Persulfate at a concentration of 1 mg/ml initiates the polymerization. We routinely omit the stacking gel used by Ornstein and Davis as it does not affect the electrophoresis patterns of our material. A discontinuous Tris *-glycine (pH 9.5) buffer (5) is used in most experiments. This buffer system provides a programmed pH change at the gel surface serving to concentrate the sample into a thin starting zone. The electrode buffer contains 3 g of Tris and 14.4 g of glycine per liter of buffer. The separating gel buffer is made up four times concentrated and contains 24 ml of $1M$ HCl, 18.15 g of Tris and 0.115 ml of N,N,N',N'-tetramethylethylenediamine per 100 ml of buffer solution. One part

* Tris = 2-amino-2-hydroxymethyl 1,3-propandiol.

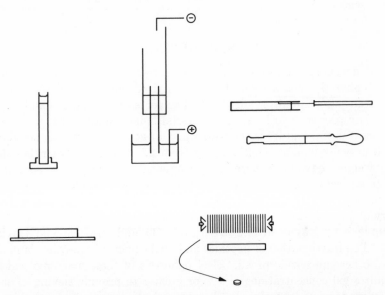

Fig. 1. Procedure for electrophoresis in dilute polyacrylamide gel. The gels are polymerized in glass tubes. The sample is underlaid beneath the electrode buffer and electrophoresed. The gel is removed by rimming and frozen. The gel is then sliced and assayed for the material being electrophoresed.

of this buffer is then mixed with 1 part of acrylamide solution ($4\times$) and 2 parts of a fresh ammonium persulfate solution ($2\times$). Water or dilute buffer is overlaid on this solution in the glass tubing to provide a flat surface after polymerization. Polymerization takes place within about 30 min. A continuous buffer at the same pH does not adversely affect the electrophoretic patterns obtained with bacteriophage. However, the electrophoresis front is harder to locate with a tracking dye, and the starting conditions are more stringent. When a continuous buffer is used the sample needs to be in a dilute buffer, and should be in a small volume. Consequently, as a matter of convenience we have used the discontinuous system except when a pH other than 9.5 was used.

The phage samples to be electrophoresed were made up in $0.05M$ Tris buffer, pH 8. The sample buffer is important. If samples of bacteriophage ϕX174 are applied to the gel in sodium tetraborate solution, a very broad band results upon electrophoresis, although the phage is more stable in borate than in Tris. Also, if the ionic strength of the sample is too high, the sample material enters the gel quite slowly and high voltage gradients are established in the gel. The sample is made up to 10% sucrose and 0.0005% bromphenol blue is added to mark the position of the electrophoretic front. The sample is then underlaid beneath the electrode buffer onto the gel. Electrophoresis is carried out at a current of 4 mA which requires a potential of about 120 V.

After electrophoresis the gel is removed from the glass tubing by rimming the gel under water with a 22-gauge cannula and forcing out the gen if necessary with a rubber squeeze bulb. The gel is placed on a microscope slide and frozen on a metal block in a Dry Ice–acetone bath. The slide is then removed and the gel sliced when it softens slightly. A set of 50 razor blades bolted together through the central holes but separated by washers is used to slice the gel. Each gel slice is separately removed from between the razor blades and placed in 1–2 ml of $0.05M$ sodium tetraborate to recover the phage from the slice. The kinetics of elution of the phage is shown in Figure 2. About 50% of the elutable phage elute within the first hour. The remainder are eluted by 10 hr. We routinely allow samples to elute overnight. The samples are then assayed for biological activity. Since the biological activity of the sample can be eluted from the gel slice complex samples such as cell lysates may be applied directly to the gel without prior purification. Samples containing as little as 10^{-13} g of bacteriophage (10^4 particles) may also be assayed. In experiments in which only the radioactivity (^{14}C or ^{3}H) was to be measured, the slices were dissolved

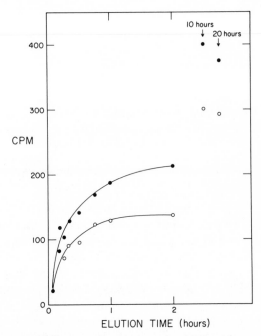

Fig. 2. Elution kinetics for the bacteriophage ϕX174. A slice containing ^{32}P-labeled ϕX was placed in 2 ml of $0.05M$ sodium tetraborate. Small samples were removed at various times to measure the quantity of phage eluted. Two slices from the same phage band were assayed.

in 20% hydrogen peroxide. If ^{32}P alone was assayed, the slices were dried on a planchet and counted.

III. ELECTROPHORESIS OF BACTERIOPHAGE

The result of electrophoresis of bacteriophage ϕX174 in a 2.6% gel at pH 9.5 is shown in Figure 3. ϕX is a small icosohedral phage with a diameter of 25 mμ, containing single-stranded DNA as its genetic material. The electrophoretic mobility relative to the bromphenol blue marking the electrophoretic front is 0.2. Recovery of infective phage particles usually ranges from 40 to 80%. In the experiment shown the recovery of infectivity was 95%. ϕX is not inactivated by the electrophoresis buffer and so is probably not inactivated during electrophoresis. The incomplete recovery may be accounted for by elution of phage from the gel surface during removal from the glass tubing. Phage samples containing from 10^4 to 10^{11} infective ϕX particles have been electrophoresed with no correlated change in band

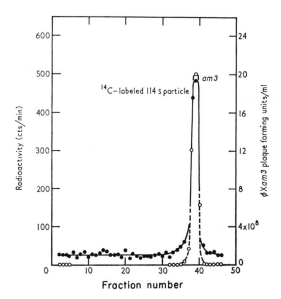

Fig. 3. Electrophoresis of radioactively labeled ϕX particles. ^{14}C-leucine labeled ϕXam3 particles were electrophoresed in a 2.6% gel at pH 9.5. Both plaque-forming units, (○) and counts per minute, (●) were assayed for each fraction.

width or recovery. Similar results are obtained when ϕX is electrophoresed in a continuous buffer system (see Fig. 4). A continuous system may be achieved either by using the same buffer in the gel as in the electrode chamber (Fig. 4, top), or by allowing electrophoresis to proceed for an hour before addition of the sample, in order to give the buffer system a chance to equilibrate (Fig. 4, bottom).

The other bacteriophage which we have electrophoresed is MS2. MS2 is approximately spherical with a diameter of 23 mμ, and contains RNA as its genetic material. MS2 moves with a relative mobility of 0.7 in our system. In the experiment shown in Figure 5, ^{32}P-labeled MS2 was electrophoresed and the fractions assayed for radioactivity. Other experiments, in which infectivity was measured, show a much sharper peak without appreciable trailing material.

IV. RESOLVING POWER OF THE SYSTEM

In order to increase the separation between particles which differ only slightly in mobility, it is sometimes useful to increase the column length. The conditions of electrophoresis are reasonably uniform for columns at least 36 cm long. The velocity of phage ϕX remained constant for a period of 24 hr. The uniformity of the electrophoretic

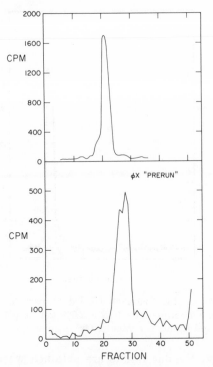

Fig. 4. Electrophoresis of ϕX particles in continuous buffers. (a) ^{32}P-labeled ϕXam3 particles were electrophoresed in a 2.6% gel at pH 9.5. The gel buffer was identical to the electrode buffer. (b) The same phage sample was electrophoresed in a gel made up with the discontinuous system. Voltage was then applied 1 hr prior to the addition of the sample.

conditions can be demonstrated by reapplying a sample to the gel at regular intervals of time, and by then measuring the positions of the bands as a function of time. This experiment was performed using hemoglobin as the electrophoretic sample, since it is visible without staining and so can be measured directly without interrupting the run. The hemoglobin velocity remained constant, except for minor irregularities, for 15 hr on a 36-cm column, as shown in Figure 6. These results concerning the uniformity of electrophoretic conditions are of interest because of the discontinuous buffer system used. It appears that the ionic conditions behind the electrophoretic front must remain relatively constant.

In order to estimate the resolution obtainable with the system it is important to determine the width of a peak produced by electrophoresis of a homogeneous sample. For this purpose we have used bacteriophage

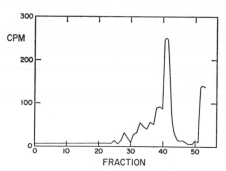

Fig. 5. Electrophoresis of radioactively labeled MS2 particles. ^{32}P-labeled MS2 particles were electrophoresed in a 2.6% gel at pH 9.5. Each fraction was assayed for counts. Previous experiments have indicated that the peak at fraction 42 corresponds to the plaque formers.

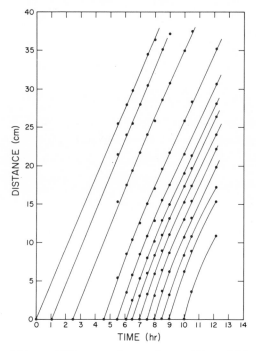

Fig. 6. Hemoglobin mobility on a long column. Hemoglobin samples were applied to a 36-cm, 2.6% gel at pH 9.5 at various times after applying the voltage across the gel. The position of each band was measured at various times to determine the hemoglobin mobility after various periods of operation.

ϕX. We take the distance between the two fractions on either side of the peak which contain one-half the number of phage present in the peak fraction as a measure of bandwidth. Bandwidth increases linearly with migration distance, as shown in Figure 7. Since we would expect band broadening due to diffusion to increase with the square root of the time of electrophoresis, it is clear that electrophoresis through the gel is responsible for at least part of the bandwidth.

This bandwidth sets the limit on the resolution of two electrophoretic peaks as long as there is no way in which the two species can be independently assayed. If two species can be independently assayed, for example, by means of two different radioactive labels or by specific bioassays, then the limiting factor in resolving two components is the accuracy with which the positions of the band centers can be determined. The uncertainty in these positions is much less than the actual bandwidth. For this reason the use of independent assays for different components can markedly increase the resolving power of the system. An example of the resolution of two biologically distinguishable mutants of ϕX with slightly different electrophoretic mobilities will be presented below.

V. PORE SIZE OF DILUTE GELS

The structure of polyacrylamide gels is poorly understood. For this reason the term "pore size" cannot at present be clearly defined in terms of a correct structural model of the gel. For a gel of any particular composition there is almost certainly some variation in pore size throughout the gel, no matter how we define the term. In order

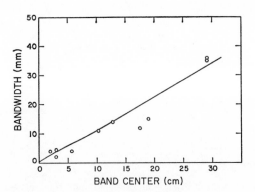

Fig. 7. ϕX174 Bandwidth as a function of distance traveled. The bandwidths for ϕXam3 particles in a 2.6% gel at pH 9.5 were measured after electrophoresing the particles various distances. ϕX requires about 24 hr to travel 30 cm.

to approach the question experimentally we will define the "critical pore size" of a gel to be the diameter of the largest particle that can be electrophoresed in the gel. In making this definition we assume that the ability of a particle to move through the gel depends only on its physical dimensions, and that other factors such as interactions of the particle surface with the gel are the same for all particles. If particles of some measured diameter, d, are electrophoresed in a series of gels of increasing polyacrylamide concentration, and the gel concentration necessary to reduce the mobility of the particles to zero is determined, then we can say that a gel of this concentration has a critical pore size of d.

The relative mobility of phage ϕX decreases linearly with increasing gel concentration and goes to zero at a gel concentration of 5.7%, as shown in Figure 8. We can therefore say that the critical pore size of a 5.7% gel is 25 mμ. Phage MS2, which has almost exactly the same diameter as ϕX (23 mμ) but exhibits a quite different electrophoretic mobility in the 2.6% gel and has a quite different appearance in the electron microscope, shows a very similar dependence of mobility on gel concentration. It also reaches zero mobility at a gel concentration of 5.7% (see Fig. 9). The excellent agreement between these two results suggests that the critical pore size as we have defined it is actually a useful parameter in discussing the behavior of these gels.

Several theoretical treatments of gel structure suggest that the pore size should be proportional to one over the square root of the gel concentration (6,7). This is an average pore size, and its relation to the critical pore size defined experimentally is not clear. However, experimental measurements of the pore size of polyacrylamide gels (8) suggest that the average pore size is proportional to one over the gel

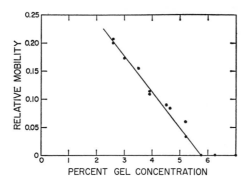

Fig. 8. ϕX174 mobility as a function of gel concentration. The mobility of ϕXam3 particles at pH 9.5 was measured for gels of various concentrations.

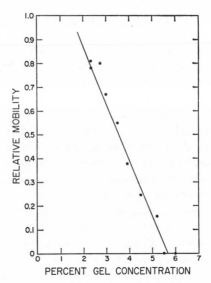

Fig. 9. MS2 mobility as a function of gel concentration. The mobility of ^{32}P-labeled MS2 particles at pH 9.5 was measured for gels of various concentrations.

concentration. In order to determine how our critical pore size parameter depends on gel concentration, it is necessary to measure mobility as a function of gel concentration for particles of different sizes.

Ferritin, with a diameter of 10 mμ, is less than half the diameter of the phages discussed above. If the critical pore size varies as one over the square root of gel concentration, then the result obtained with the phages ϕX and MS2 predicts that a 36% gel would be required to reduce the ferritin mobility to zero. If, on the other hand, the critical pore size is proportional to one over the gel concentration, then the ferritin mobility should reach zero at a gel concentration of 14.2%. The experimental results with ferritin show a linear decrease in mobility with increasing gel concentration as in the case of the phages. The mobility reaches zero at a gel concentration of 11%, as is shown in Figure 10 (solid circles). This result clearly shows that the critical pore size is not proportional to one over the square root of the gel concentration, but is approximately proportional to one over the concentration. Assuming that the critical pore size is inversely proportional to the gel concentration, we can estimate the critical pore size for a 2.6% gel by extrapolating from a critical pore size of 25 mμ at a gel concentration of 5.7%. The critical pore size calculated in this way for a 2.6% gel is 50 mμ. Phage λ does not penetrate into a 2.6% gel. This phage has a head 54 mμ in diameter and a tail 140 mμ long.

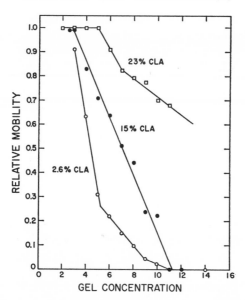

Fig. 10. Rabbit ferritin mobility as a function of gel concentration. The mobility of rabbit ferritin at pH 9.5 was measured for gels of various concentrations. These mobilities were measured in gels with various crosslinking agent to monomer ratios; (○) 2.6% CLA/total gel; (●) 15% CLA/total gel; (□) 23% CLA/ total gel.

Half-tail fibers from T4 also do not penetrate into a 2.6% gel. These are rod-shaped particles about 4 mμ in diameter and 65 mμ long. Apparently the fibers do not orient themselves and "snake" their way through the gel structure.

This critical pore size at which the particles no longer penetrate the gel is apparently quite a bit larger than the average pore size. The average pore sizes calculated by White from the water permeability of polyacrylamide gels range from 3.6 mμ at 5% to 1 mμ at 35% (9).

The proportion of crosslinking agent in the gel is an important factor in determining the dependence of mobility on gel concentration. For a given gel concentration the mobility of ferritin increases as the proportion of crosslinking agent is increased (see Fig. 10). Plots of mobility versus gel concentration for varying proportions of crosslinking agent have quite different shapes, being very nearly linear for gels containing 15% crosslinking agent, and becoming nonlinear for both higher and lower proportions of crosslinking agent. Since neither the structure of the gel, nor the way in which mobility depends on the structure of the gel, is understood, it is not possible to interpret these results at present. They may, however, prove useful in some applications of separation by size.

VI. HYBRID PHAGE PARTICLES

As an example of the results which can be obtained with this technique, we would like to present some of our results concerning the structure and maturation of the bacteriophage ϕX.

Mutants of ϕX exist with mobilities different from that of wild type. Several strains had previously been separated by sucrose density gradient electrophoresis by Aach (10). Four electrophoretically different ϕX strains separated at pH 9.5 on a 2.6% gel are shown in Figure 11. The fast strain is a temperature-sensitive mutant while the two slow strains are host-range mutants. The two host-range mutants can be shown to be electrophoretically distinct on a longer gel. On a 5-cm gel we occasionally see a nonrepeatable one-fraction difference between

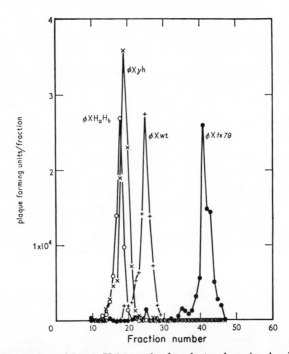

Fig. 11. Separation of four ϕX174 strains by electrophoresis. A mixture of the four ϕX strains was separated by electrophoresis on a 2.6% gel at pH 9.5 The various strains were identified by their distinctive plaque types when plated on a mixed bacterial indicator and then incubated at 30°C for 3 hr before being shifted to 40°C.

strains; the 11-cm gel in Figure 12 shows a clear separation of these two strains.

The isolation of electrophoretic variants of phage ϕX can be very useful in the structural analysis of a complicated particle. Consider the cell shown in Figure 13 mixedly infected with two electrophoretically "labeled" phage types. It is known from previous work that when broth-grown cells are mixedly infected with two ϕX strains, both genotypes may be represented in the progeny of a single cell (11). If mature virus particles are assembled by a random withdrawal of coat subunits from a pool containing two types of protein, one might expect the production of hybrid phage coats. If the subunits produced by the two parental strains have different charges, then the hybrid particles should comprise a set of particles representing all of the intermediate charges and hence mobilities between the parental types. The result of electrophoresing the progeny from *E. coli* C mixedly infected with ϕXH$_a$H$_b$ and ϕXwt is shown in Figure 14. A marker phage with wild-type mobility was added to the progeny before electrophoresis. Clearly hybrid particles were produced.

Hybrid phage also resulted from cells mixedly infected with ϕXts79 and wt as shown in Figure 15. The phage must therefore be assembled by withdrawing subunits randomly from a pool shared by both coinfecting phage types.

Information concerning phage structure as well as maturation can

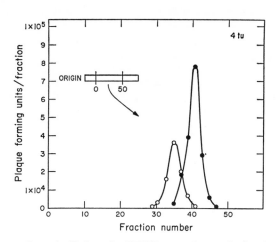

Fig. 12. Separation of ϕXγh and ϕXH$_a$H$_b$ on a long gel. A mixture of ϕXγh, (○) and ϕXH$_a$H$_b$, (●), was separated by electrophoresis on a 11-cm, 2.6% gel at pH 9.5. A section from the center of the gel was removed and sliced. The two strains were assayed by plaque type.

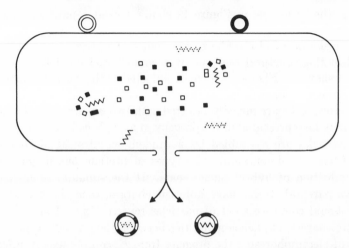

Fig. 13. A mixed infected cell. The parental phage types would be represented here with a black protein coat and a solid DNA or with a white protein coat and a dotted DNA. The smaller squares are meant to represent protein subunits in the pool from which components for phage assembly are drawn.

be deduced from such hybrids. The electrophoretic variant H_aH_b is an extended host range mutant. The extended host range capacity is known to be a property of the phage coat. One can then ask how pure the coat of a hybrid phage must be in order to retain this extended host range capacity. In an electrophoretic separation of hybrid phage the particles with various ratios of extended host range to wild-type subunits have been fractionated. By plating the hybrids on the resistant host the number of phage with the extended host range capacity can be measured. Table I illustrates the bioassay used to measure

TABLE I

The plating properties of the host range mutant. ϕXH_aH_b and ϕXwt. The extended host range mutant ϕXH_aH_b will lyse the *E. coli* strain C_1 while ϕXwt will not. Both lyse C. A mixed indicator of *E. coli* C and C_1 will therefore distinguish between the two phage types.

Phage particle		Plating properties	
DNA	Protein coat	On C_1	On mixed indicator
H_aH_b	H_aH_b	Plaque	Clear plaque
H_aH_b	WT	No plaque	Clear plaque
H_aH_b	Hybrid	?	Clear plaque
WT	H_aH_b	No plaque	Turbid plaque
WT	WT	No plaque	Turbid plaque
WT	Hybrid	No plaque	Turbid plaque

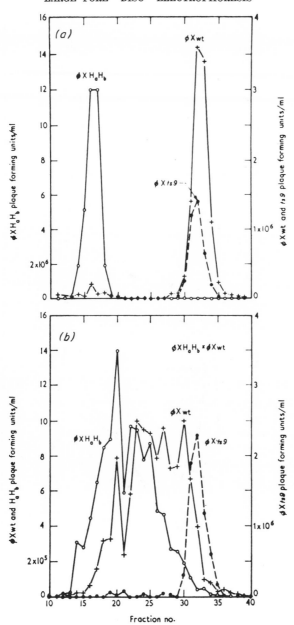

Fig. 14. Phenotypic mixing between ϕXH$_a$H$_b$ and ϕXwt. (a) Electrophoresis of a mixture of ϕXH$_a$H$_b$, ϕXts9 (not derived from a mixed infection). (b) Electrophoresis of the progeny from cells mixedly infected with ϕXH$_a$H$_b$ and ϕXwt. ϕXts9 was added as a marker. (○) ϕXH$_a$H$_b$; (—+—+—) ϕXwt; (●) ϕXts9.

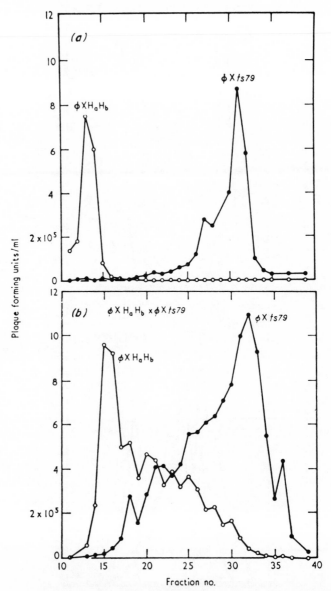

Fig. 15. Phenotype mixing between ϕXH$_a$H$_b$ and ϕXts79. (a) Electrophoresis of a mixture of ϕXH$_a$H$_b$ and ϕXts79 (not derived from a mixed infection). (b) Electrophoresis of the progeny from cells mixedly infected with ϕXH$_a$H$_b$ and ϕXts79. (◯) ϕXH$_a$H$_b$; (●) ϕXts 79.

this number and the number of phage with the H_aH_b genotype. Figure 16 shows these numbers for each fraction from an electrophoretic fractionation of H_aH_b, wt and H_aH_b, ts79 hybrids.

Clearly the coat needs to be largely H_aH_b to retain its extended host range capabilities. The proportion of phage with the extended host range genotype that also have the extended host range phenotype in each fraction is consistent with what one would expect from a single attachment site made up of five subunits (4). This value agrees well with the idea that ϕX adsorption occurs at one of the 12 vertices of the virus. Since a fivefold rotational axis passes through each vertex, we might expect a cluster of five subunits at this point.

VII. ϕX COAT PROTEINS

The identification of the electrophoretic variants has greatly facilitated our studies concerning the ϕX coat proteins. ϕX has a reasonably complicated structure. Electron micrographs of the phage show it to be an icosahedron with a projection or spike at each fivefold vertex. A negatively stained ϕX preparation is shown in Figure 17. The genetic evidence indicates that there is more than one portein in the whole phage (12). Many bands are observed when ϕX is disrupted in $8M$ urea and electrophoresed on a small pore acrylamide gel. Four strong bands can be seen at pH 3.5 in the presence of mercaptoethanol as shown in Figure 18. We have been able to show that the "slowest" protein is the capsid protein. The "fastest" protein in the group near the top of the gel is the major spike component, and the intermediate protein is most probably a minor spike component (13). These proteins can be identified using the whole-phage electrophoretic mutants. The simplest assumption would be that an electrophoretically variant phage would contain a mutant protein which would also be electrophoretically variant. The pattern of proteins obtained from the electrophoretically slow mutant H_aH_b shows an altered protein pattern (Fig. 19). It is gratifying that the protein apparently altered is also slower than the wild-type protein. Since we feel from physical studies that this protein is in the spike we can associate the host range function with a specific phage structure. The spike should exhibit fivefold symmetry as it is at the vertex of the icosahedron. This fits well with the five subunits previously deduced to be present on the attachment site.

An altered pattern is also obtained with another mutant, ts79. ϕXts79 is an electrophoretically fast whole-phage mutant, and it shows a fast protein component. That there is also a residual component at

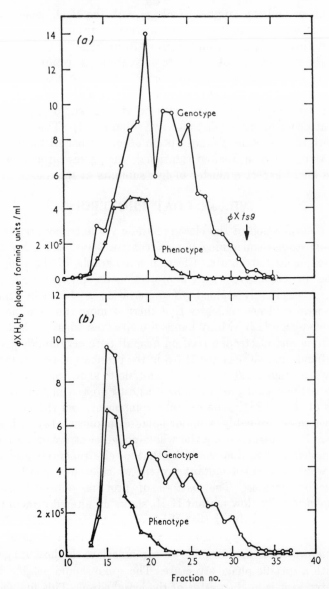

Fig. 16. Assay of hybrid phage particles on C_1. (a) ϕXH_aH_b,wt hybrids. ($\triangle$) phage titer on C_1; ($\bigcirc$) titer of total H_aH_b genotype, reproduced from Figure 14b. (b) ϕXH_aH_b,ts79 hybrids. ($\triangle$) phage titer on C_1; ($\bigcirc$) titer of total H_aH_b genotype, reproduced from Figure 15b.

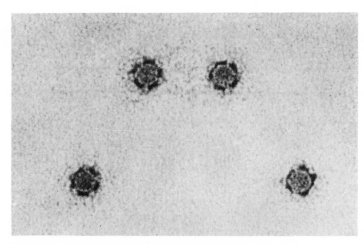

Fig. 17. Electron micrograph of φXam3 particles. φXam3 particles were negatively stained with uranyl acetate.

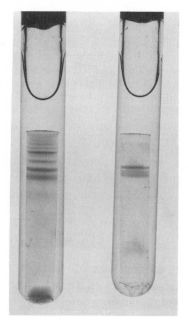

Fig. 18. Electrophoresis patterns of the φX proteins produced by 8*M* Urea disruption of the phage. φXam3 particles were disrupted in 8*M* urea for 2–6 hr at 30°C. The disruped phage were then electrophoresed on a 7% gel containing 8*M* urea at pH 3.5. The sample shown on the right contained 5% mercapto-ethanol during disruption.

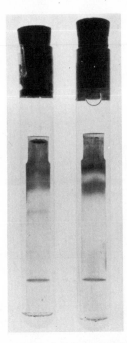

Fig. 19. Electrophoresis patterns of the proteins from ϕXam3H$_a$H$_b$ and ϕXam3. The phage particles were disrupted in $8M$ urea in the presence of 5% mercaptoethanol at 30°C for 2–6 hr. The disrupted phage were then electrophoresed on a 7% gel containing $8M$ urea at pH 9.5. The left pattern is from ϕXam3. The right pattern is from ϕXam3H$_a$H$_b$.

the wild-type position is not yet explained. It may be yet another protein. The phage preparation from which these patterns were obtained is electrophoretically homogeneous. The ts79 mutation is in cistron III, so the protein with the altered mobility can be identified as the cistron III product.

VIII. SUMMARY

In summary, it is clear that complex particles such as viruses may be electrophoresed to advantage in dilute polyacrylamide gels. The technique is simple, repeatable, and uses relatively inexpensive equipment. pH's other than that discussed may be used. The gel structure may be altered by changing the quantities of monomer and crosslinking agent employed. Phage were easily eluted allowing the advantages of the bioassay to be utilized. Long columns may be used, but band spreading reduces the number of components which can be distinguished on such

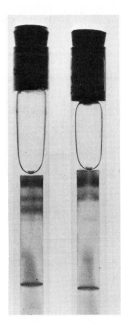

Fig. 20. Electrophoresis patterns of the proteins from φXam3 and φXam3ts79. The phage particles were disrupted and electrophoresed as were the particles shown in Figure 20. The left pattern is from φXam3. The right pattern is from φXam3ts79.

columns. It should be possible to electrophorese particles up to about 50 mμ in diameter.

Acknowledgments

We acknowledge the capable technical assistance of Barbara Jo Winter. We would like to thank John Newbold for a ^{32}P-labeled φX174 preparation, Jane Harris Cramer for a ^{32}P-labeled MS2 preparation, Samuel Ward for a T4 half-fiber preparation, and Michael Nesson for a rabbit ferritin preparation. This work was supported in part by grants RG6965 and GM13554 from the U.S. Public Health Service. One of us (MHE) acknowledges support from U.S. Public Health Service fellowship 5-F2-AI-28,658-02.

References

1. S. Raymond and L. Weintraub, Science, 130, 711 (1959).
2. L. Ornstein and B. J. Davis, Disc Electrophoresis, Parts 1 and 2, Distillation Products Industries, Rochester, New York, 1962.
3. S. Hjerten, S. Jerstedt, and A. Tiselius, Anal. Biochem., 11, 211 (1965).
4. C. A. Hutchison III, M. H. Edgell, and R. L. Sinsheimer, J. Mol. Biol., 23, 553 (1967).

5. B. J. Davis, *Ann. N. Y. Acad. of Sci.*, **121**, 404 (1964).
6. L. Ornstein, *Ann. N. Y. Acad. Sci.*, **121**, 404 (1964).
7. S. Raymond and M. Nakamichi, *Anal. Biochem.*, **3**, 23 (1962).
8. M. P. Tombs, *Anal. Biochem.*, **13**, 121 (1965).
9. M. L. White, *J. Phys. Chem.*, **64**, 1563 (1960).
10. H. G. Aach, *Z. Naturforsch.*, **186**, 290 (1963).
11. M. J. Yarus, *J. Virol.*, **1**, 135 (1967).
12. R. L. Sinsheimer, C. A. Hutchison III, and B. J. Lindqvist, *The Molecular Biology of Viruses*, Academic Press, New York, 1967, pp. 175–192.
13. M. H. Edgell, C. A. Hutchison III, and R. L. Sinsheimer, Biophys. J. *8* abstracts A64 (1968).

Differential Elution of Trapped Macromolecules

M. Sung * and O. Smithies

Laboratory of Genetics, University of Wisconsin, Madison, Wisconsin

The separation and characterization of biological macromolecules forming subcellular particles has been approached in our laboratory by a new procedure. The particles are trapped in gel and their various components are then differentially eluted with solutions which cause progressively greater dissociation of the complexed components. By choosing a suitable gel for the trapping, some components can be completely retained in the gel.

We have described the principle of our procedure elsewhere (1). Here we discuss in detail the construction of the apparatus, and illustrate its use to examine the histones eluted from gel-trapped nuclei from rat livers. In a later paper (2) we will describe the use of the procedure to study the *in vivo* and *in vitro* synthesis and phosphorylation of histones from the nuclei of regenerating livers.

The differential elution of histones from gel-trapped nuclei yields histones free from contamination with nucleic acid. The completeness of this separation is made possible by the fact that histones are relatively small macromolecules, compared with DNA, and will pass through acrylamide gels leaving the DNA physically entrapped. Further resolution of the heterogeneous mixture of histones follows from the use of salt gradients during the differential elution.

The method of differential elution of trapped macromolecules can

* Present address: Department of Biochemistry, University of British Columbia, Vancouver 8, Canada.

be carried out with very small amounts of material, and should have many applications other than those described below. The dissociating agents we used for eluting histones from nuclei were acid and salt solutions. Many others, such as urea, detergents, organic solvents, and increased temperature, could equally well be tried in other situations. The trapped particles and macromolecules might also be treated while in the apparatus with suitable enzymes or chemicals to release covalently bound components, or to facilitate the dissociation of complexes.

I. GENERAL PROCEDURE

The method has several stages. First, nuclei are isolated in a high degree of purity. The nuclei are then trapped in a constant diameter thread of polyacrylamide gel which is packed into a small column. Histones are eluted from the trapped nuclei with several concentration gradients of small volume and are collected in uniform fractions in the 50 μl range. Both the gradient-generating and fraction-collection systems are governed by cam-driven syringes in a mechanical device specially designed for this purpose (Fig. 1). Samples obtained are characterized in a suitable starch–gel electrophoresis system.

II. NUCLEI

Rat livers are perfused with dilute sucrose solution and homogenized in a 2.2M sucrose medium containing 0.03M MgCl$_2$ and buffered with phosphate (0.02M) at pH 6.8. The homogenates are layered over 2.2M buffered sucrose medium and the nuclei are sedimented at approximately 90,000 g for 20 min. Figure 2 shows a phase contrast photomicrograph of the resulting nuclei. More details of this isolation procedure are given in our previous publication (1).

III. MACROMOLECULAR TRAPPING PROCEDURE

Three stock solutions are required. Solution a, kept at room temperature, is 50 g Cyanogum (#41 Gelling Agent, E. C. Apparatus Corp., Philadelphia, Penn.) made up to 100 ml with water. Solution b, kept in ice, is a saturated aqueous solution of riboflavin diluted with two parts of 2.2M sucrose medium. Solution c, kept in ice, is 2.2M sucrose medium diluted with two parts of water.

To trap nuclei in acrylamide threads, the purified nuclei, suspended in approximately 0.2 ml of ice-cold 2.2M sucrose medium, are thoroughly mixed with 0.2 ml of solution a. Then, 0.2 ml of solution b is added and mixed, and the total volume is taken up into a 1-ml

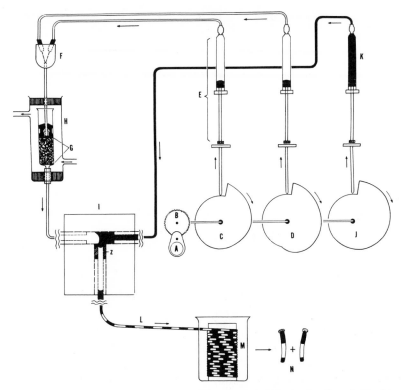

Fig. 1. Clock motor A and gear B drive two gradient cams C and D whose followers push the syringe pistons E. The syringe contents are delivered to a mixing chamber F and pass to a column G containing nuclei trapped in acrylamide threads; the column is cooled in a water jacket H. The column effluent passes to a hollowed out "T" in a polyethylene or lucite block I with a glass insert Z and is separated into fractions by light oil delivered by the linear cam J and oil syringe K. The fractions are stored in a polyethylene coil L held at about 4°C in a bath of light oil M. Individual microfractions N are obtained by cutting the polyethylene coil in the oil segments and sealing the tubes with hot forceps.

syringe. Sufficient volume of solution c is then taken up to give a total of 0.8 ml, and the syringe contents are well mixed by inversion. The syringe is then wrapped with aluminum foil to exclude light. The polymerization of the mixture is by a light-catalyzed reaction, which appears to be speeded up by the presence of sucrose.

Gel threads for controlled elution should be small in diameter; suitable threads are obtained with 0.015 in. diam polyethylene tubing

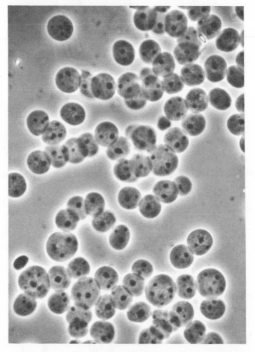

Fig. 2. Purified rat liver nuclei (40× phase objective).

which fits a 26-gauge needle. About 50 cm of tubing are wrapped around a General Electric F4T5.CW fluorescent light source ((A) in Figure 3) which is placed in a cryostat set at −30°C, as shown in the figure. The fluorescent light generates sufficient heat to make it necessary, in addition to using a cold chamber, to funnel a stream of cold air onto the coil from a funnel (B) containing Dry Ice.

About 0.05 ml of the nuclei and acrylamide mixture is injected gently from the shielded syringe (C) into the polyethylene coil up to a few turns from the end. Three to five minutes is allowed for polymerization to begin in the coil before extrusion. To test for adequate polymerization, the mixture in the coil is moved slightly and the meniscus is inspected; if it is irregular, and a slight resistance can be felt as the mixture is pushed, the polymerization is properly underway. Occasionally resistance to extrusion may be due not to gel polymerization but to freezing of the contents in the small segments of the tubing which are not immediately adjacent to the light source. Gentle stroking with a warm finger is sufficient to defrost any such small frozen segments. Once polymerization has started, the mixture is gently ex-

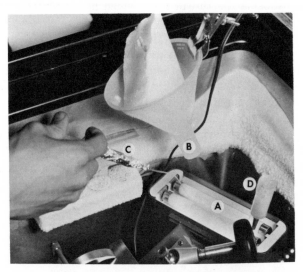

Fig. 3. Trapping the nuclei in polyacrylamide gel.

truded. Care should be taken to avoid premature extrusion but the polymerization should not be allowed to go to completion before starting to extrude. One continuous thread can usually be obtained when a gentle and continuous pressure is applied to the syringe plunger. Polymerization and extrusion of 0.8 ml of mixture takes about an hour. The extruded thread of gel is collected in a column (D) containing $0.14M$ NaCl at pH 5. In the event that the polymerization is too extensive, cutting the coil into pieces will permit recovery of the gel thread.

In some of our earlier experiments we trapped the nuclei in agar, both in bead and in thread forms. To do this, 3% Special Agar Noble (Difco Laboratories, Detroit, Michigan) prepared according to Claflin and Smithies (3) is mixed rapidly with the suspension of nuclei at 45°C to give finally a 2.2% agar solution. The mixture is taken up in a 1-ml syringe surrounded by a 45° water jacket. To prepare beads, the mixture is sprayed via a 26-gauge needle through the air into a beaker containing ice-cold solvent over a lower layer of buffered $0.44M$ sucrose medium (1 part of $2.2M$ sucrose medium diluted with 4 parts of water). The solvent permits the gelation of the spheres before they settle into the lower phase of buffered sucrose. Figure 4a shows a phase contrast photomicrograph of the agar beads containing trapped nuclei. The beads are clearly of unequal sizes, which is likely to cause uneven elution, and the recovery is relatively poor. In addition beads occasionally pack to give very slow flow rates. These drawbacks are eliminated by using the thread form which has a constant cross-sectional area, virtually total recovery, and yields a column which cannot easily be overcompressed. Agar threads are made by extruding the liquid agar mixture through a small piece of polyethylene tubing (internal diameter 0.015 in.) with the distal few centimeters immersed in ice-containing medium. The gelling time with agar is very short and a gentle but steady force applied to the syringe plunger yields a single thread of agar-trapped nuclei. The necessity of maintaining the agar mixture at 45°C causes some undesirable changes in the case of nuclei and histones. Consequently our final choice is acrylamide polymerized at low temperatures. The resulting thread is no different in appearance from the agar one shown in Figure 4b.

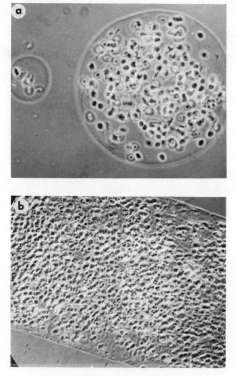

Fig. 4. Nuclei trapped in agar beads and threads.

IV. GRADIENT MACHINE

Batchwise elution of histones from the trapped nuclei constitutes an effective and simple purification procedure for isolating histones free from nucleic acid contamination. However, since histones are very heterogeneous, it is much more advantageous to effect some preliminary fractionation by using a gradual dissociation process. This is effectively carried out by using a continuous salt concentration gradient to elute the histones from the column of gel-trapped nuclei.

Conventional gradient generating devices do not permit the short gradients and slow flow rates needed for the present microscale elution method. We consequently have developed a device having adjustable flow rates upward from about 0.00074 ml/min and able to generate reproducible gradients of volumes 1.6 ml and upward. The principle of our machine has been described (1). Two liquids are delivered at variable rates from syringes whose plungers are moved by helical cams. The cams are cut according to mathematical functions which generate the desired shape of the gradient yet maintain the total eluant flow constant.

The gradient machine * has the following components illustrated in Figure 5: column assembly (E); gradient cams (F); cam followers (G); clock motor and gear (H); top plate syringe assembly (I); mixing chamber (J); fraction collection system (K).

Column Assembly. The column (L, Fig. 6) is made from a 10-ml B-D disposable syringe (Becton, Dickinson and Co., Rutherford, N.J.) cut down to about half its length. Four tight-fitting stainless steel 100 mesh screens (M) are wrapped in lens paper (N) and used to sandwich the gel threads inside the column. The rubber part of the syringe plunger (O) is inverted and fitted to a 2-in. length of Tygon tubing (internal diameter 0.02 in.) by means of a cemented piece of larger diameter Tygon tubing (P). The other end of the tubing connects to the mixing chamber of the gradient machine. The glass column jackets (Q), 3½ in. long × 1½ in. in diameter, are mounted on a back panel of the gradient machine and can be individually or serially connected to a refrigerated constant temperature circulator bath.

The acrylamide threads are extruded into the column with the two bottom screens already in place. The column is then topped with the second pair of screens, and the modified rubber plunger assembly is put into position and forced down slowly to compress the gel threads to a final volume of 1–1.2 ml (for 0.8–0.9 ml of initial mixture). Excess

---

* Available commercially from O. Hiller Co., P.O. Box 1294, Madison, Wis. 53701.

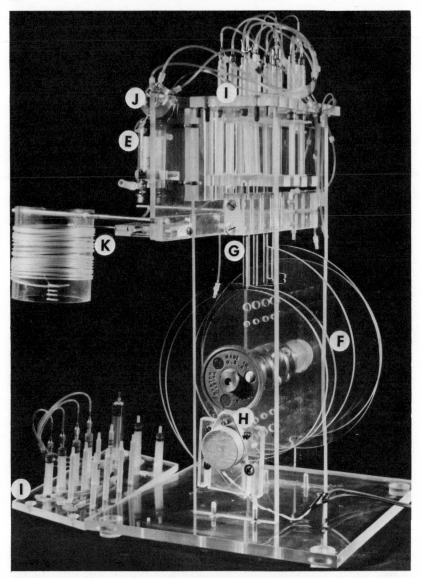

Fig. 5. General views of apparatus (parts of fraction collection system omitted for clarity).

liquid is allowed to flow out of the bottom of the column or back out through the upper Tygon tube. Care is taken to avoid forcing the threads through the screen or trapping air in the column. The upper Tygon tube from the column is clamped off with a hemostat and the

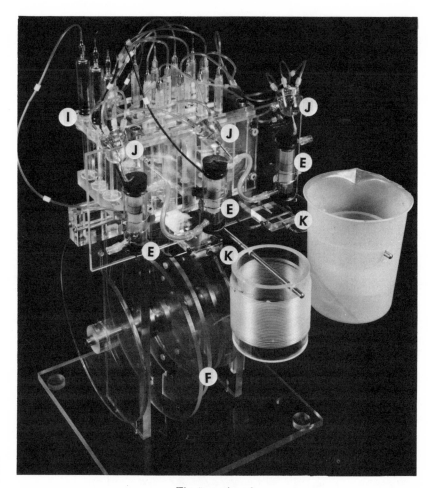

Fig. 5 continued.

column is then inserted into the glass jacket through which 0°C water is circulated.

Gradient cams. For the present purposes we constructed two sets of linear gradient cams (F) each on 180° of a circle but 180° out of phase with respect to each other. This arrangement permits two linear gradients to be delivered one after another during one complete revolution of the cams. Many odd-shaped functions can be approximated by two successive linear gradients (see Fig. 7) and we have not found it necessary to have more complex gradient cams made.

The cams were cut to an accuracy of approximately 0.001 in., using

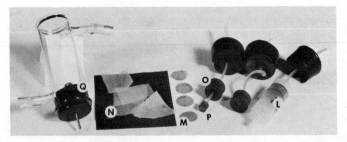

Fig. 6. The column assembly.

an indexing head on a vertical milling machine. They were milled from smaller to larger diameter and for every ¼° the cut was reset. The maximum rise of each cam is 1.8 in.

The accuracy of the cams was tested by measuring the linearity of the resultant gradient with two concentrations of dye, taking samples at various stages during the operation. The result (Fig. 8) shows that the linearity is correct to within the experimental accuracy of the optical density measurements.

Cam Followers. A cam follower (G) rides on each cam and provides up-strokes for up to three syringe plungers. This permits one, two, or three columns to be eluted simultaneously, each with the two independent linear gradients. (In most of the illustrations we show only one column in position, in order not to obscure details.)

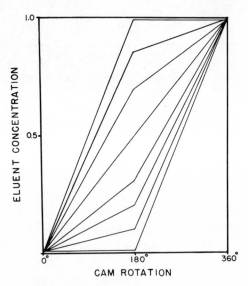

Fig. 7. Gradients obtainable with two pairs of linear cams.

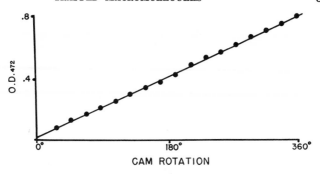

Fig. 8. Test of the linearity of the two cam pairs.

Clock Motor and Gears. The entire mechanism is driven by a synchronous clock motor and gear (*H*). Many discrete flow rates can be achieved through various combinations of syringe sizes, different speed motors, and gears (see Tables I, II, and III).

Top Plate Syringe Assembly. To further increase the versatility of the machine, the syringe assembly (*I*) is replaceable (see Fig. 5) so that different volumes of gradient can be generated by using different sizes of syringes. Table I shows the gradient volumes that can be generated by using the readily available Plastipak B-D disposable syringes. Tables II and III indicate the value of the corresponding flow rates with two convenient electric clock motors geared down 1:12.

The top plate, when placed on the top of the machine, is supported at its corners by four strong compression syringes (see Figs. 5 and 14) which act against four screws. These springs ensure controlled contact between the syringe plungers and cam followers during the setting-up, so that there is no lag in delivery of the contents of the syringes when the cams begin to rotate.

Mixing Chamber. Since it is desirable to have the least practical mixing volumes in a microgradient system, special mixing chambers (*J*) were made by casting into a block of plastic four 27-gauge stainless hypodermic needles which converge and communicate with the outflow tube—a 1-in. length of 16-gauge stainless steel tubing. Appro-

TABLE I

Possible Gradient Volumes for Each 180° of Cam [a]

Syringe size, ml	1	2½	5	10	30	50
Gradient volumes, ml	1.6	5	10	14	34	50

[a] The second 180° of cam can use a different size of syringe from the first 180°.

TABLE II

Flow Rate Ranges

Syringe pairs [a]	Motor speed, rpm	Total gradient time, hr	Total gradient volume, ml	Flow rate, ml/min
0–1	1/360	36	1.6	
1–1	1/360	72	3.2	0.00074
0–2½	1/360	36	5	
2½–2½	1/360	72	10	0.0023
0–5	1/360	36	10	
5–5	1/360	72	20	0.0046
0–10	1/360	36	14	
10–10	1/360	72	28	0.0064
0–30	1/360	36	34	
30–30	1/360	72	68	0.0157
0–50	1/360	36	50	
50–50	1/360	72	100	0.023

[a] 0 implies use of only 180° of total cam rotation.

priate connections are made with Tygon tubes to the column and from the syringes of the gradient machine.

Fraction Collection System. A fraction collection system permitting the column effluent to be obtained in discrete fractions of about 50 μl was devised. The fractions are kept separate by light oil (6 vol-

TABLE III

Flow Rate Ranges

Syringe pairs	Motor speed, rpm [a]	Total gradient time, hr	Total gradient volume, ml	Flow rate, ml/min
0–1	1/60	6	1.6	
1–1	1/60	12	3.2	0.0044
0–2½	1/60	6	5.0	
2½–2½	1/60	12	10.0	0.0138
0–5	1/60	6	10	
5–5	1/60	12	20	0.0276
0–10	1/60	6	14	
10–10	1/60	12	28	0.0384
0–30	1/60	6	34	
30–30	1/60	12	68	0.0942
0–50	1/60	6	50	
50–50	1/60	12	100	0.138

[a] Other commercially available motor speeds are as follows: 1/30, 1/20, 1/12, 1/6, 1/3, 5/12, 1/2, 2/3, 5/6, and 2 rpm.

umes of Amosol, American Oil Co., and 19 volumes of silicone D.C. 550, Dow Corning, colored with Oil Blue N, Allied Chemical); they are stored in a polyethylene tube. Alternating segments of column effluent and the light oil are obtained by connecting the column to one of the two horizontal arms of a hollowed-out T in a polyethylene or Lucite block which wets with the oil. An oil-delivering syringe is connected to the other horizontal arm. A glass insert, which wets with the column effluent, is placed in the outflow arm of the T (the "vertical" arm which is actually horizontal during use).

The differences in wetting properties of oil and water for the several parts of the T-block are critical for its operation as a fractionator. Figure 9 shows a reconstructed version of the sequence of events in the T. In (a) the effluent is passing out through the glass insert and continues to do so until the oil completely blocks the outflow arm (b). Oil then flows out (c) until column effluent interrupts the flow (d). Effluent then passes out of the block (e) and the operation cycles again through (a). This ordered alternation of phases keeps the fractions discrete as shown in Figure 10a.

Individual microfractions are obtained by cutting the polyethylene coil in the oil segments between the effluent fractions. A pair of hot

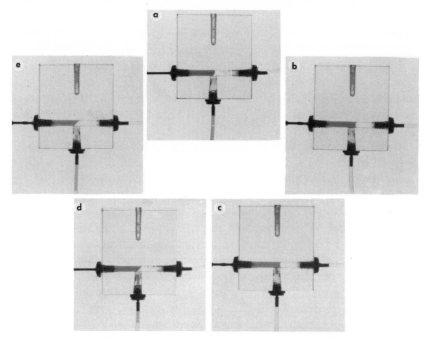

Fig. 9. Sequence of events in fractionator T-block.

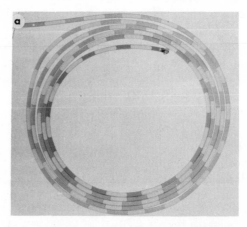

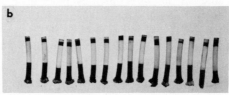

Fig. 10. Part of the fraction storage coil, and some individual fractions cut from it.

forceps is used to seal the polyethylene tubes (Figure 10b). The fractions can be inserted into corrugated paper for convenient storage.

The microfractions are usually regular in size, but occasionally trouble is encountered with the wetting properties of the components causing the fractions to be uneven. In this case, cutting the collecting coil into segments of equal length will permit the recovery of comparable fractions.

Fractions can be freed of contaminating oil by extruding them onto a small square of Parafilm. The oil wets the Parafilm while the aqueous phase forms a droplet which can easily be taken up, free of oil.

The volumes of the fractions are controlled by the dimensions of the T-block. In Figure 11a the internal diameter of the outflow arm is plotted against the fraction size and in Figure 11b the square of the radius of the horizontal arm is plotted against fraction size. The T-block dimensions for any desired fraction volume, within limits, can be obtained from these graphs. In practice, fractions of approximately 50 μl are convenient for many purposes; these are obtained with horizontal arms of diameter 0.129 in., and a vertical arm of diameter 0.150 in. with a glass insert having a bore of about 0.05 in.

The fractionator block can be made from polyethylene or Lucite.

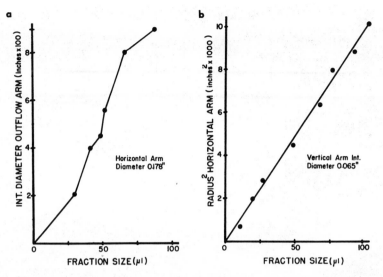

Fig. 11. The effects of the T-block dimensions on fraction size.

Connections to the three arms are made via 18-gauge stainless steel tubing soldered into screws fitted with O-rings (see Fig. 9).

A single oil cam is used to pump the oil for the fraction collector. This cam need not be cut as precisely as the gradient cams; ours was hand plotted and hand milled to an approximately linear function with a maximum cam rise of 1.7 in. (1.9 in. would be better). The oil syringes, like the gradient syringes, are interchangeable but are preferably of the glass type. The following combinations are convenient. For the 3.2-ml gradient (obtained with four 1-ml syringes; flow rate 0.26 ml/hr) a 2.5-ml oil syringe with a 1.9-in. cam rise gives a flow rate of 0.22 ml/hr; for a 10 ml gradient (obtained with four 2½ ml syringes; flow rate, 0.83 ml/hr) a 10-ml syringe is used to give a corresponding flow rate of 0.70 ml/hr.

The gradient cams need to be checked initially and occasionally thereafter for proper alignment. To do this a ¼ in. steel rod is passed through four holes in the gradient cams as shown in Figure 12a (these holes were aligned at the time of cutting the cams). If the rod fails to pass through any hole, the corresponding cam is out of alignment, and should be loosened from the shaft as shown in Figure 12b to permit its realignment. The alignment procedure is important since without it the proper proportioning of the two solutions and the linearity of the resultant gradient will be disturbed.

The cam assembly is turned to its starting position and put into

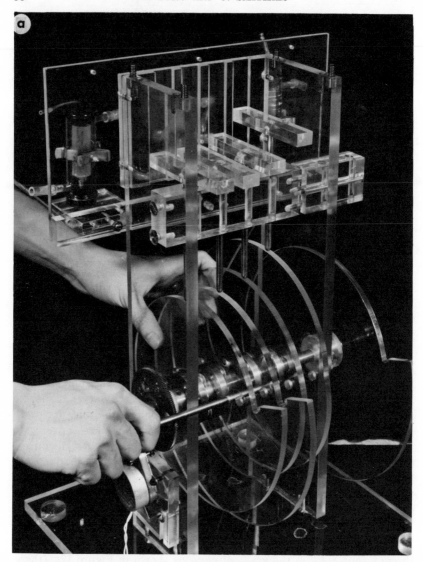

Fig. 12. Testing and readjusting the alignment of the cams.

gear with the clock motor. The syringes in the top plate assembly are then loaded in an upright position by withdrawing the salt and acid solutions from their respective bottles via the tygon connecting tubes as shown in Figure 14. Air bubbles are expelled by pushing the plungers in and out several times. The glass oil syringes are loaded with the light oil mixture by pouring it into the syringes, since the oil

Fig. 12 continued.

Fig. 13. Securing the top plate syringe assembly.

mixture is too viscous to be drawn into syringes easily without entrapping small air bubbles which interfere with the proper functioning of the T-block.

The top plate syringe assembly is then placed on the machine and is secured with four screws which are tightened successively against the corresponding compression springs (Fig. 13) in small increments. As mentioned above, this procedure keeps the syringe plungers in close and continuous contact with the cam followers and obviates any lag in their responses to the cam rotation.

The mixing chambers must be washed thoroughly with the first solution used for elution before connecting them. The tubings from the syringes are then connected to the corresponding mixing chambers. Leakage can be avoided by greasing the connectors with silicone grease, or by using Luer-lock connectors on all tubings.

The collection coil, a long piece of polyethylene tubing (internal diameter 0.02 in.), is wrapped around a drum and immersed in a bath of Amosol (cooled if necessary). The coil is prefilled with the light oil mixture. Prefilling the coil is necessary to make it wet with oil

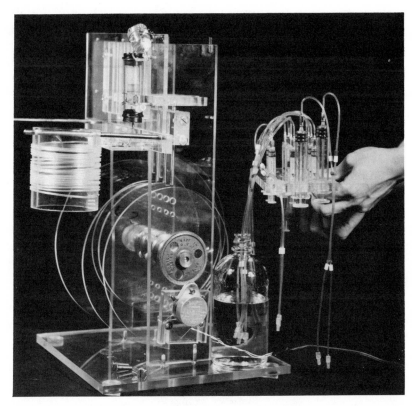

Fig. 14. Loading the eluant syringes.

and help maintain an approximately constant pressure in the whole system during operation. The exterior Amosol bath is needed to prevent loss of solvent by diffusion through the polyethylene tube during the time of elution. Without Amosol in the oil phase the fractionator parts do not wet properly, and the storage coil functions poorly. Too little Amosol causes free small oil droplets to occur in the coil; too much Amosol can cause the merging of fractions in the coil.

Prior to each run the T-block is cleaned with detergent, rinsed with water and the horizontal arm is dried thoroughly. A thin film of heavy oil (machine oil or white oil) is applied to the horizontal arm which is to be connected to the oil syringes. Special care is taken not to grease the lip of the glass insert or the other horizontal arm. The greasing ensures proper wetting. Each T is filled with water or buffer solution and is connected to its respective oil syringe, column outflow tube and collecting coil. No air bubbles should be trapped in the T.

When more than two consecutive gradients are to be used for elution, the machine requires resetting up after the first two. The top plate assembly is removed, after clamping off the mixing chamber outflow tubes, by disconnecting the inlet tubings from the mixing chambers. The cams are returned to start, the syringes are refilled, and connections are remade; it is usually not necessary to wash out the mixing chambers.

V. RESULTS

The reproducibility of the whole procedure and its application to very small quantities of material are illustrated in Figure 15, from our previous paper (1). Two separate experiments were carried out with nuclei prepared from rat livers 24 and 36 hr after partial hepatectomy. The columns were prewashed for 12 hr with 10 ml of 0.14M NaCl, pH 5, and eluted with four successive salt gradients of 5 ml each. The resultant histones were examined by starch–gel electrophoresis. The

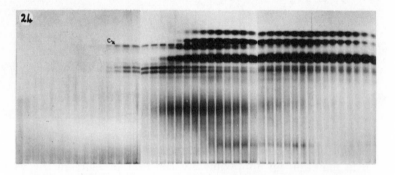

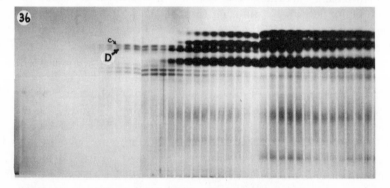

Fig. 15. Starch–gel electrophoresis results of the histones eluted from trapped rat liver nuclei 24 and 36 hr after partial hepatectomy.

reproducibility of the procedure is obvious, yet the method can detect differences (note the presence of D in the 36 hr experiment, and its absence 24 hr posthepatectomy). The microscale of this procedure is clear, since the total nuclear DNA in each of the two experiments was of the order of half a milligram.

Acknowledgments

This paper (paper #1241) from the Laboratory of Genetics, University of Wisconsin, was supported by the National Institutes of Health (GM 15422) and the National Science Foundation (GB 4362).

M. S. was supported by the Public Health Service Pre-Doctoral training grant [GM 398(05-80)] and by the American Cancer Society Grant (T66D). At present time M. S. is a Research Fellow of the Helen Hay Whitney Foundation, New York.

We thank Mr. Otto Hiller and the late Mr. Art Olson for help with the design and construction of the gradient machine. We are particularly grateful to Mr. Jerry Hartzberg for his interest and care in taking many of our photographs.

References

1. M. Sung and O. Smithies, *Biopolymers,* **7,** 39 (1969).
2. M. Sung and O. Smithies, "Phosphorylation and synthesis of histones," manuscript in preparation, 1968.
3. A. J. Claflin and O. Smithies, "Antibody-producing cells in division," *Science,* **157,** 1561 (1967).

The Application of Free-Flow Electrophoresis to the Separation of Macromolecules and Particles of Biological Importance

K. Hannig

*Max-Planck-Institut-für Eiweiss- und Lederforschung,
Munich, Germany*

A method for the separation of mixtures of substances known as "continuous deflection electrophoresis" has been developed over the past 17 years and is in principle applicable to all classes of substances that are electrically charged and therefore migrate in an electric field. The problem has always been the search for suitable experimental conditions and apparatus designed to exploit this principle. I will give a brief review of the development of our apparatus to the carrier-free model and I shall conclude with a few examples of applications of the principle that have only been made possible by recent apparative developments.

The principle of deflection electrophoresis is illustrated in Figure 1. A solution of an electrolyte of suitable pH streams in a direction perpendicular to the lines of force of an electric field. The mixture of substances to be separated is injected continuously from a given point at a fixed rate into the streaming medium. The various components of the mixture migrate sideways over different distances according to their electrophoretic mobility and can thus be collected at different

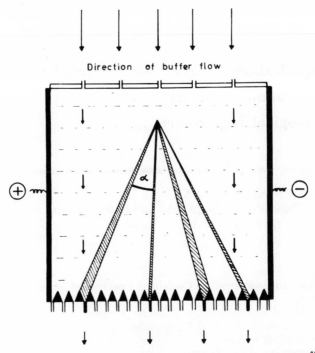

Fig. 1. Principle of continuous deflection electrophoresis. $\tan a = \dfrac{ui}{q\kappa w}$, where $u =$ Electrophoretic mobility. $i =$ Electric current. $q =$ Cross section of the electrophoresis chamber. $\kappa =$ Specific conductivity of the buffer. $w =$ Streaming velocity of the buffer solution.

positions at the end of the separating chamber. As the velocity of the streaming buffer film and the strength of the electric field can be varied experimentally over a wide range, it is in principle possible to obtain any desired angle of deflection. The general laws of electrophoretic migration give the expression for the angle of deflection:

$$\tan a = \frac{ui}{q\kappa w}$$

where u is the electrophoretic mobility, i is the electric current, q is the cross section of the electrophoresis chamber, κ is the specific conductivity of the buffer, and w the streaming velocity of the buffer solution. It is clear from the diagram that precautions must be taken to ensure laminar and uniform buffer flow and that a homogeneous electric field prevails, in order to assure constant working conditions over long periods of time.

We are aware of the fact that the easiest way of stabilizing the streaming fluid would be by means of a porous carrier. Here there are basically two techniques. In the first the separating chamber is a very shallow cuvet filled with sea sand, glass beads, or some other granular material; and in the second normal filter paper or heavy filter paper serves as the carrier material. Designs with shallow separation chambers were described for the first time nearly simultaneously by us (1) and by Svensson and Brattsten (2). These designs have been developed further by these two groups and by Winsten, Friedman, and Schwarz (3). The apparatus developed in our laboratory has a separating chamber which is roughly 30 cm long, 20 cm wide, and only 0.8 cm deep. It is cooled at both sides. Uniform buffer flow is ensured by the use of multichannel pumps, and there are membranes between the separating chamber and the electrode chambers. This equipment has been used chiefly for the separation of mixtures of proteins. Twenty-five milliliters of serum can be fractionated in it per day. It was not easy to maintain strictly parallel flow in these cuvets owing to disturbances due to gas bubbles formed by electroosmotic and polarization effects. Only the filter paper devices were successful in practice as they were less complicated and less subject to disturbing influences. A large number of designs using normal filter paper (4,6) or heavy filter paper (5,7) as carrier material have been described in the literature and some of these are also commercially available.

Figure 2 gives a general view of our apparatus (5). The separating surface is 42 cm wide and 40 cm long. The carrier is kept in a moist chamber. An effective cooling system that will not be described in detail here permits the use of very thick filter papers giving a very high throughput. The capacity of this design is about 200 mg of sample mixture per day rising to 5–10 g per day for those models using heavy filter paper. One must, however, always bear in mind certain limits to the field of application of designs using porous carriers, limits that depend on their physical and chemical properties. First of all there are adsorption effects that may complicate or prevent the separation of even low molecular weight samples if they have a high affinity for the carrier material, and disturbing adsorption and filter effects are inevitable in the case of very high molecular substances such as fiber proteins, hemocyanins, and viruses, or with materials of extreme particle size such as cells, cell organelles, or bacteria. For these reasons it had not previously been possible to apply deflection electrophoresis to the fractionation of these biologically interesting and important classes of substance. The complications arising from the use of porous media such as the contamination of the fractionated material by solu-

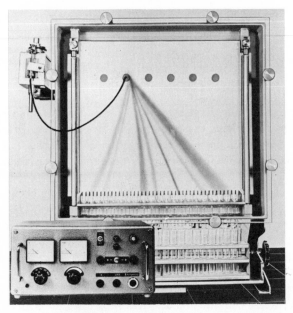

Fig. 2. Continuous electrophoresis apparatus with filter paper as the carrier
material (from Hannig, ref. 5).

ble degradation products of the carrier material further limit this
technique.

For these reasons we started investigating the possibility of performing the deflection electrophoresis in a freely streaming fluid. Here,
however, completely laminar flow can only be achieved by the use of
relatively complex equipment. It is essential to avoid the turbulence and convection caused by vibrations and temperature differences. Figure 3 is a simplified diagram of the apparatus in which we
succeed in maintaining laminar flow (8). The shallow electrophoresis
chamber consists of two parallel glass plates 50 × 50 cm, accurately
ground plane to a thickness of 5 mm and spaced 0.5 mm apart. The
outer surfaces of the glass plates are strongly cooled by blowing cold
air onto them in a countercurrent in order to compensate for the Joule
heat generated during the electrophoresis. This method of cooling has
proved very suitable, being not only effective and safe but also very
constant. Thermal convection can be completely avoided by posi-
tioning the chamber nearly horizontal.

Homogeneous buffer flow is achieved by the following two devices.
First, the buffer solution is injected at constant and equal rates at six

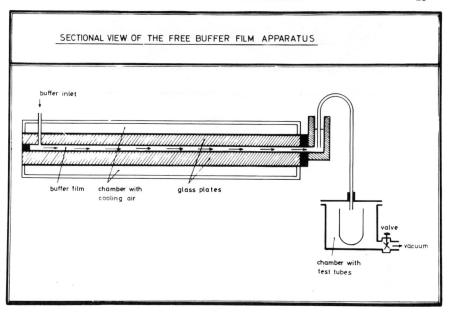

SECTIONAL VIEW OF THE FREE BUFFER FILM APPARATUS

buffer inlet

buffer film   chamber with   glass plates
               cooling air

valve
vacuum

chamber with
test tubes

Fig. 3. Separating chamber of the free-flow electrophoresis apparatus (cross section).

equidistant points using a six-channel pump. Second, the fractions are collected in very small vessels which are in pressure equilibrium with one another through the separation chamber, and are therefore filled at equal rates, thus ensuring uniform flow in the chamber. When the little vessels are full, they are simultaneously emptied into larger containers by suction. This apparatus permitted the first successful free flow electrophoresis under completely stationary conditions over longer periods of time.

Figure 4 gives an overall view of the separating apparatus, the electrophoresis chamber with the inlet and outlet for the cooling air, the electrode chamber, and a chamber in which the fractions obtained may be kept cool. The sample mixture is kept cool in a part of the chamber also included in the overall insulation and is injected into the separating chamber in a continuous stream by a small dosing pump. In the lower half of the picture we see the rectifier with its switchboard and the cold air generator. Migration in the chamber proceeds along linear paths that can be kept extremely narrow and diffusion is surprisingly low.

A few examples of the separation of proteins will be discussed next.

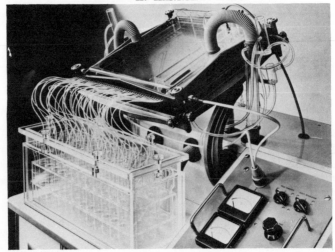

Fig. 4. Continuous free-flow electrophoretic apparatus (from Hannig, ref. 8).

I. SERUM PROTEINS

Figure 5 shows a typical spectrum of a separation of serum proteins. Of the 150-odd distinct serum proteins, only about one-fifth have as yet been obtained in pure form and characterized electrophoretically. In view of this heterogeneous composition it is not surprising that the

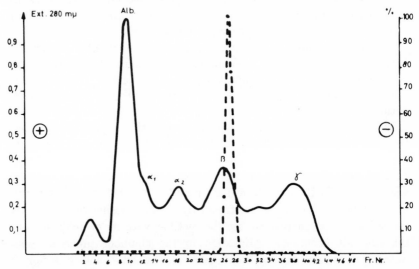

Fig. 5. Separation of serum proteins. Binding of $^{59}FeCl_3$ to transferin. (——) OD at 280 mμ (protein). (— — —) per cent of maximum radioactivity. pH 8.6; 2300 V; 160 mA [Fröhlich (9)].

protein distribution spectrum is not completely resolved and that the minima do not fall to zero. In an investigation of the bonding of iron to transferrin, undertaken in collaboration with the laboratory of Bennhold in Tübingen (9), $^{59}FeCl_3$ was added to the serum. After the electrophoretic separation only a very narrow band of fractions in the β_2 region showed radioactivity. The iron is thus only bound to the transferin migrating in the β region. The serum could also have been fractionated using carrier electrophoresis, but the surprising sharpness of the peak of the radioactive component allows it to be isolated completely in the free-flow apparatus. Owing to the high separating efficiency, it is possible to fractionate up to 40 ml of serum per day in this apparatus.

Seitz and Eberhagen (10) have investigated the action of fractions of normal serum and serum from diabetics, obtained under similar conditions, on the enzyme system of pigeon liver, which synthesizes fatty acids in the fractions that migrated rapidly on electrophoresis. The normal serum was found to contain one component that strongly promoted the incorporation of ^{14}C from acetate solution into the long-chained fatty acids and two components that inhibited it. A further strongly inhibiting component with high migration velocity was found in the serum from diabetics.

Bidwell et al. (11) were able to isolate the antihemophilic factor VIII free of fibrinogen from human and cow plasma using free-flow electrophoresis. The authors nearly always used borate buffer of pH 8.47 in the separation.

II. ANIMAL AND PLANT PRODUCTS CONTAINING PROTEINS AND NUCLEIC ACID

Due to its high throughput and delicate mode of action, free-flow electrophoresis has been used with success for the isolation of animal and plant proteins with high biological activity. New results were obtained, especially with those classes of material that could only be separated in carrier-free systems because of their high molecular weight or strong adsorbing properties.

Waldschmidt-Leitz and Kling (12) were able to isolate homogeneous components from the prolamines of various types of grain. As an example Figure 6 shows the separation of ϵ-hordein in barley prolamines. It is of interest that the first half of the fractions of ϵ- and δ-hordein (fractions 18–22) contain only the ϵ component. This was proved by careful purity tests.

In the course of work on the isolation and characterization of hemag-

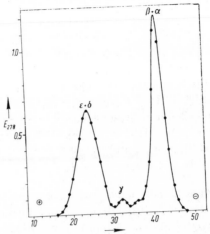

Fig. 6. Separation of ε-hordein in barley prolamins (12). $1N$ acetic acid; 2350 V; 145 mA.

glutinins that cause allergic reactions (13) we succeeded in performing an extensive separation and a protein chemical and immunological characterization of the carbohydrate-containing proteins in kidney beans (*Phaseolus vulgaris*). Eleven protein components could be prepared in pure form by prefractionation in ammonium sulfate and subsequent electrophoresis. At least two of the components proved to be hemagglutinins with high activity.

Synge and co-workers (14) did some most systematic experiments on the isolation of plant proteins using free-flow electrophoresis. In the extraction and electrophoretic separation the authors used well-chosen buffer systems such as phenol–acetic acid–water in equal parts. Usually basic proteins are easily soluble in this buffer system and are present in an unaggregated state. The electrophoretic separation of proteins from nucleic acids obtained from extracts of fresh plant leaves is particularly successful.

Sarkar (15) describes a complete preparative separation of RNA and the preparation of pure native tobacco mosaic virus proteins. The virus sample (5–50 mg/ml) is dialyzed at 0–4°C for 24 hr against a 0.05–0.01M glycine–NaCl–NaOH buffer of pH 10.3–10.6 and subsequently centrifuged at 100,000g. The electrophoretic separation of TMV *vulgaris* in glycine–NaCl–NaOH buffer is illustrated in Figure 7. The protein yield was 90%, and it was shown to be in the native state by virtue of its ability to aggregate at pH 5.

The separation of nucleotides and their derivatives by free-flow

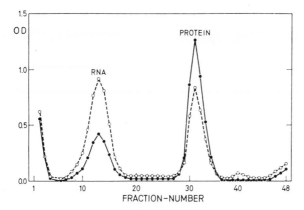

Fig. 7. Separation of RNA and the preparation of pure native tobacco mosaic virus protein (15): 0.017M Glycine–NaCl–NaOH buffer; pH 10.5; 1400 V, 100mA.

electrophoresis is described by Sulkowski and Laskowski (16). Figure 8 shows the well resolved separation of four desoxymononucleotides at pH 3.5 and 2500 V. Figure 9 shows the separation of adenosine mono-, di-, and triphosphate at pH 5.0. The authors obtained equally good results with the separation of digestion products of thymus DNA with micrococcal nuclease, as illustrated in Figure 10. All components were of high purity and were suitable for subsequent spectrophotometric investigations. In this way these investigators were able to identify and determine quantitatively the terminal groups in short oligonucleotides.

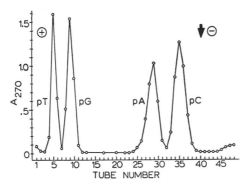

Fig. 8. Separation of desoxyribonucleotides (16): 0.15M Ammonium acetate, pH 3.5; 2500 V; 100 mA.

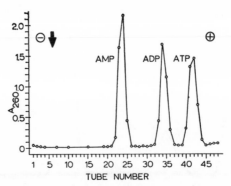

Fig. 9. Separation of AMP, ADP, and ATP (16). 0.05M Ammonium acetate, pH 5.0; 1400 V, 155 mA.

III. ENZYMES

As it does not induce any chemical changes in even sensitive biological materials, free-flow electrophoresis is also an elegant method for preparing enzymes in pure form and for enriching enzyme solutions. Figure 11 shows the separation of a crude elastase fraction (17). The sample is an acetate extract of pancreatin that has been prepurified to an activity of 17.5 elastase units by precipitation with ammonium sulfate. The chief contaminating proteins could be removed by electrophoresis at pH 7.6 in the presence of small amounts of Ca²⁺ ions yielding a specific activity of 220 elastase units. This is a 13-fold purification with a total yield of 96% in a single step. The activity of the freeze-dried fraction was more than 25% higher than that of the most active preparations described in the literature to date. As a

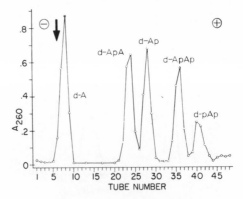

Fig. 10. Separation of d–A, d–Ap, d–ApA, d–ApAp, and d–pAp (16). 0.05M Ammonium acetate, pH 5.0; 1600 V; 180 mA.

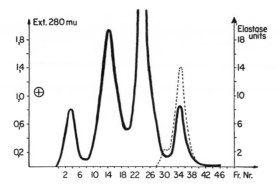

Fig. 11. Purification of a crude elastase fraction (17) (from pancreatin). (——)
OD 280 mμ (protein). (– – –) Elastase activity, pH 7.6; 2000 V; 160 mA.

further example of the purification of an enzyme, Figure 12 shows the
fractionation of a commercially available collagenase (18). In this
case it was not possible to separate the component with collagenase
activity from a component with amidase activity. Yet the removal
of a very large portion of the other proteins present permitted an eight-
fold enrichment of the collagenase activity with a virtually 100% yield
of the initial activity.

An interesting result was obtained in the purification of a cerebroside sulfatase from pig kidney [Mehl and Jatzkewitz (19)]. After
the final purification step, which was free-flow electrophoresis, it was
found that the full cerebroside sulfatase activity could only be obtained
after recombining two high molecular weight electrophoresis components, one possessing aryl sulfatase activity while the other was enzymatically inactive. The enzyme extract suitable for electrophoresis
was prepared from the mitochondrial fraction of the kidney homoge-

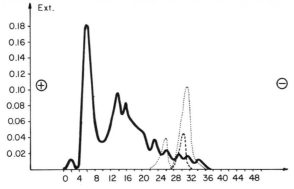

Fig. 12. Fractionation of a commercially available collagenase (18). (——)
OD 280 mμ (protein) (– – –) Collagenase activity. (. . .) Amidase activity. Tris
buffer, pH 8.9; 1700 V, 210 mA.

nate by precipitation in acetone and centrifugation. The overall enrichment of the specific activity was 6000-fold after recombination.

Further enzymes that have been successfully purified with the aid
of continuous free-flow electrophoresis are a proteinase from *Aspergil-
lus* and a new peptidase from kidney extract reported by Nordwig and
Jahn (20), serum cholinesterase by Gürtner (21), and the enzyme
citrate synthase by Wieland (22). Finally Lynen and co-workers (23)
were able to isolate an isopentenyl-*P*-*P*-isomerase of high activity
from yeast. It should be added that the pharmaceutical industry has
also begun to use free-flow electrophoresis for the purification of some
of its enzyme preparations (24).

IV. MATERIALS OF EXTREMELY HIGH MOLECULAR WEIGHT

Great difficulties have always been encountered in the isolation of
very high molecular materials such as fibrous proteins or acid mucopolysaccharides. The isolation of collagen, for example, is not possible
in heterogeneous systems and was first performed by free-flow electrophoresis. The fibrous collagen is solubilized in the native form by
treatment with pepsin. This splits the crosslinks leaving the so-called
tropocollagen monomers with a molecular weight of 350,500 and a
rodlike shape with a length of 2850 Å. The complete removal of the
pepsin was essential for the further investigation of this soluble collagen (Fig. 13). Apart from the main components collagen and pepsin
(distribution of activity), there are two additional small fractions that

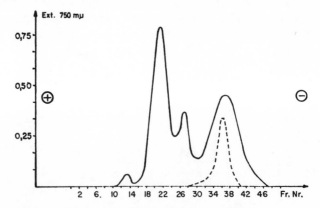

Fig. 13. Collagen after treatment with pepsin (ratio of components 2:1). (———)
Protein (Lowry, 750 mμ). (– – –) Pepsin activity 1*N* acetic acid pH 2.4; 2250 V,
100 mA.

have not yet been examined more closely. François and Glimcher (25) have recently described the isolation of the three chains of collagen with the aid of free-flow electrophoresis. The starting material was acid-soluble collagen from codfish skin and calf skin and collagen from chicken bones (Fig. 14). After separating the α and β components on Biogel P-300, the α component was fractionated into the α_1, α_2 and α_3 chains at 4°C and pH 5.25 in the presence of $6M$ urea. The amino acid composition was also determined. This technique thus permits the isolation of large enough amounts of the individual chains to begin sequence investigations.

On digesting connective tissue such as skin with pronase one obtains a raw tissue extract that contains mainly the acid polysaccharides. The otherwise very difficult purification of these mixtures becomes relatively simple and the yield is high (26). Figure 15 shows the result of a separation by continuous free-flow electrophoresis and gives the experimental conditions. Mashburn and Hoffman (27) undertook a systematic investigation of the conditions for separating mucopolysaccharide–protein complexes. These authors used $0.5N$ acetic acid as medium for the separation of hyaluronic acid and chondroitin sulfate. A $0.03M$ acetate buffer of pH 5.0 was found to be suitable for the fractionation of cartilage extracts and of mucopolysaccharides. The field strength was usually between 30 and 40 V/cm.

Figure 16 illustrates the fractionation and purification of substances of larger particle size, in this case the single-stranded DNA phage of *E. coli*. A more intensive investigation of this threadlike phage which

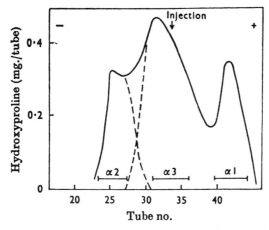

Fig. 14. Separation of the α components of calf-skin collagen (25). Trimethylacetic acid pH 5.25 in $6M$ urea.

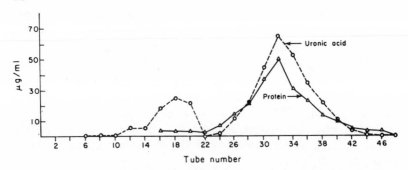

Fig. 15. Separation of mucopolysaccharides (26) (rat skin). 1N acetic acid + 0.5N formic acid, 2000 V; 140 mA.

has a molecular weight of about 10 million is at present underway in the labs of Dr. Braunitzer and Dr. Hobom at the Max Planck Institute for Biochemistry in Munich. In collaboration with our Institute, conditions for the fractionation by free-flow electrophoresis were found that permitted the isolation of tiny amounts of a mutated phage (28). The mutant was identified by a plaque test. Note the logarithmic scale of this distribution curve: the scale of the ordinate covers six orders of magnitude, which means that the peak would be several miles high on a linear scale. It was possible to culture the mutant after its

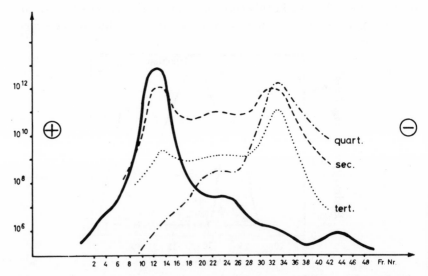

Fig. 16. Purification of DNA Phage fd (28) biological test: Plaque-forming units. Acetate buffer, pH 4.6; 1900 V; 190 mA.

electrophoretic separation without change in its electrophoretic mobility. It should be mentioned that other methods of separation such as column chromatography or carrier electrophoresis would, at this time, have failed because of the high molecular weight of the phage.

V. SEPARATION OF CELLS AND CELL ORGANELLES

For some time we have been working on the preparative separation of cells and cell organelles. Preliminary experiments have shown that a mixture of rabbit and human erythrocytes, for example, can be separated by free-flow electrophoresis with surprisingly high resolution. If, however, the apparatus is used in the horizontal or slightly tilted position which ensures high stability of the buffer film, a contamination of the lower glass plate by sedimenting particles cannot be avoided and the separation is brought to a halt fairly quickly. The use of the separating chamber in the vertical position with the sedimentation in the direction of the fluid flow is usually associated with great experimental difficulties. Disturbances due to thermoconvection occur very easily. However, using novel small batteries, based on the Peltier effect, that transform electric current directly into refrigerating power, it was possible to obtain an extremely homogeneous temperature in the vertical chamber.

We have built two models based on this principle. One has separation chamber dimensions of 50 × 50 cm, the thickness of the buffer film being 0.5 mm (29). The width of the chamber makes this apparatus most suitable for the separation of substances with very different mobilities together with particles with very similar electrophoretic mobility. Owing to the relatively low streaming velocity of the buffer film of about 30 min to 1 hr for 50 cm, differences in sedimentation behavior can also be utilized to separate particles or cells with equal surface charge. The other model has a considerably narrower separation chamber, only 12 cm wide with a length of 50 cm and buffer film thickness of 1 mm. Figure 17 shows an overall view of this apparatus (29). The cooling batteries receive their power from an electronically regulated rectifier. The high-voltage rectifier that maintains a constant electric field has a current stabilizer. In the center is a chamber for the fractions which can also be cooled. The fractions are collected via 90 tubes arranged about 1.3 mm apart across the end of the chamber by a 90-channel pump. This allows separation at high resolution even with high buffer film velocities of, for example, 1–5 min/45 cm. This is particularly useful for the separation of sensitive cell mixtures.

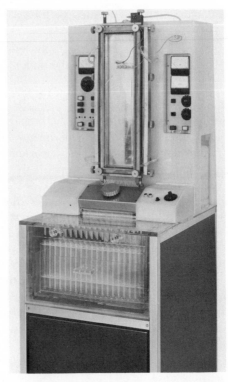

Fig. 17. Free-flow electrophoresis apparatus with vertical separation chamber (29).

We obtained similar results with the separation of cells and cell fragments of animal and plant origin. Very mild and well-defined experimental conditions are necessary for their purification and separation. Apart from mechanical forces, osmotic influences and pH differences in the suspension medium can damage the sample. Suitable osmotic conditions are usually obtained using 0.25–$0.35M$ cane sugar solution (analytically pure). In general all operations should be performed rapidly and at temperatures below 5°C. Even brief warming can cause an irreversible inactivation of complicated systems. The preparation of cells from biological material is particularly easy if they are not bound in an organ or in tissue. Often, as in the case of blood cells, a simple sedimentation experiment suffices for separation, but we have very little experience in the electrophoretic isolation of cells from tissue. At all events care must be taken not to alter the surface charge of the particles by, for example, adsorption of proteins from the already hemolyzed cells or adsorption of complexing electrolyte ions.

A. Separation of Cells

Figure 18 illustrates the separation of blood cells. This shows the migration of rabbit and human erythrocytes injected into the chamber as a mixture (30). The experiment has, of course, no practical value but does show clearly (a) how sharp the zones remain during the separation and (b) how characteristic the differences are between cells of the same type from different species.

In reproducible runs we were able to show that the preparative separation of cells from human blood into erythrocytes, lymphocytes, granulocytes, and monocytes is quite feasible by free-flow electrophoresis. Figure 19 shows a typical distribution curve obtained for the enrichment of leucocytes by sedimentation (30,31). The erythrocytes that were still present were removed by NH_4Cl hemolysis. The electrophoretic separation was carried out in a phosphate–saccharose–EDTA buffer of pH 7.1. In the fractions obtained the cells were differentiated and counted. A surprising result is that the distribution curves for the granulocytes and for the lymphocytes; both show two peaks. In addition to the main granulocyte fraction a relatively small fraction of electrophoretically more mobile granulocytes of quite normal morphology is also present and in addition to the normal relatively mobile lymphocytes there is a larger type of lymphocyte, the cells showing slightly variable staining behavior. We have since been

Fig. 18. Separation of rabbit and human erythrocytes (30) pH 6.9; 1200 V; 230 mA.

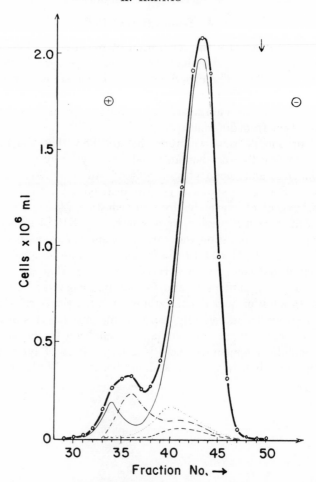

Fig. 19. Separation of human leucocytes (31). (———) Granulocytes. (– – –)
Lymphocytes.

able to show that antibody-producing cells are concentrated in this
fraction. We obtained similar results on fractionating spleen cells.
The fractionated cell material proved to be 70–80% vital and of normal
morphology. Figures 20 and 21 show stained smears of the main fractions, normal lymphocytes, and 98% pure granulocytes, respectively.

In further experiments we separated cells of Walker Ascites tumor
in rats from added erythrocytes and unaltered leucocytes in continuous electrophoresis (32). Figure 22 shows a micrograph of the stained
smear of the Ascites material before the separation. In addition to the
erythrocytes and the various forms of leucocytes one can recognize

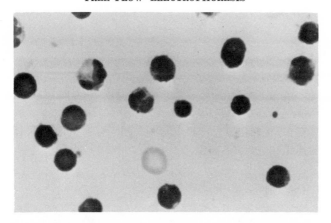

Fig. 20. Micrograph of the stained smear of the lymphocytes (31).

the characteristic morphology of the tumor cells quite clearly. On electrophoretic fractionation one obtains a component that consists only of erythrocytes. Figure 23 is a photograph of the erythrocyte fraction. In the slowly migrating leucocyte fractions we obtained 90% enriched tumor cells in a very narrow region. Figure 24 shows the cells of this fraction. All the fractions separated were implanted into animals. Only the fraction enriched in tumor cells caused a cancer.

B. Separation of Cell Organelles

A number of technical difficulties arose in the course of our experiments on electrophoretic separation and isolation of cell organelles.

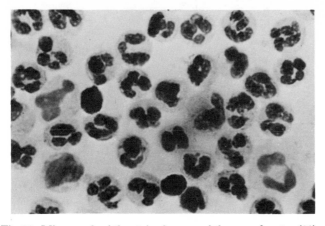

Fig. 21. Micrograph of the stained smear of the granulocytes (31).

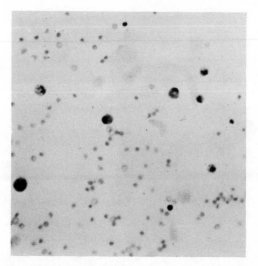

Fig. 22. Ascites cells before the separation (32).

The necessary use of isoosmotic buffer systems that contain an electrolyte often leads to the formation of aggregates which have to be avoided, particularly for electrophoretic operations. The best experimental conditions have to be chosen to suit the individual behavior of the various cell materials. As electrophoresis of a cell homogenate can never produce a complete fractionation, simply because of the large

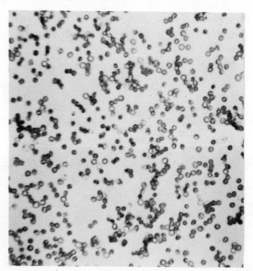

Fig. 23. Erythrocytes isolated from Ascites material (32).

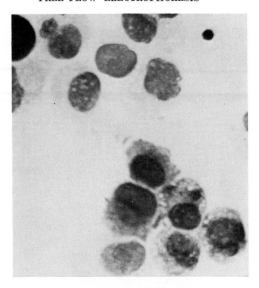

Fig. 24. Tumor cells (32).

variety of particles and soluble components, we prefer to start with a simple prefractionation in the ultracentrifuge. Although very good fractionation procedures using density gradient centrifugation to isolate cell organelles have been described recently, we still believe that our combination is a less harmful, more rapid procedure and gives higher yields.

An example is the electrophoretic purification of liver ribosomes (Fig. 25). The ribonucleoprotein particles were obtained by ultracentrifugation and resuspended. Electrophoresis was then performed at pH 7.0–8.5 at a field strength of 40 V/cm, removing the soluble impurities such as glycogen, ferritin, hemoglobin, and membrane fragments (33). The resulting sample was shown to be free of adsorbed proteins by comparing the absorption at 260 and 235 mμ (1.6–1.65). The picture obtained from the analytical ultracentrifuge showed that the ribosomes were chiefly present in the 80S form. In collaboration with Matthaei et al. (34) we were able to separate ribosomes of *E. coli* from their subunits (30 and 50S particles). Subunits charged with polyuridylic acid also showed different electrophoretic mobilities. These observations lead one to hope that a further fractionation will be possible which would permit the isolation of the various states through which the ribosomes go during the protein biosynthesis.

The preparation of subcellular particles from plant cells which retain their biological activity is more difficult than the preparation from

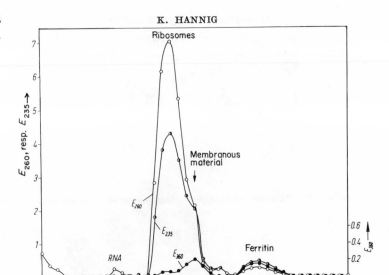

Fig. 25. Purification of a crude ribosome fraction (33) 0.04M Tris; pH 8.0; 2200 V; 110 mA.

animal cells. Little work has therefore been done on this field. Our electrophoretic experiments in this field have been concentrated on the isolation of homogeneous chloroplast fractions from young spinach leaves and of chloroplast fragments with differing chlorophyll a/chlorophyll b ratio (35). Figure 26 is an electron micrograph of sections of a homogeneous chloroplast fraction obtained by this method. Further

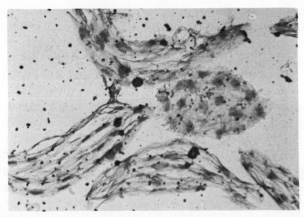

Fig. 26. Electronmicrograph of sections of a homogeneous chloroplast fraction (35).

results suggest that the lipoprotein complex can be brought into solution with detergents and that it will be possible to separate the photoactive pigment systems I and II electrophoretically.

VI. FREE-FLOW ELECTROPHORESIS AS AN ANALYTICAL RESEARCH METHOD

In the examples described free-flow electrophoresis served mainly for the preparative purification of components of mixtures. The method is, however, also gaining importance for solving analytical problems. It is possible to make the separation chamber almost arbitrarily small, to perform the separation on a micro scale and to evaluate the results qualitatively and analytically by some optical or other physical procedure.

Strickler et al. (36) have described an application in which they separated various strains of bacteria and pigments and evaluated the results photographically. A development by Kolin (37) must also be mentioned in this connection. He described an apparatus for free-flow electrophoresis in which the buffer film is caused to spiral slowly in a cylindrical shell by a combination of electromagnetic and electric fields.

We have set up a small separation chamber roughly 5×20 cm which is essentially equivalent to the large apparatus described. The plates are, however, made of quartz glass. The results are evaluated as follows. A beam of light illuminates a narrow band across the width of the chamber. The image is enlarged (or reduced as required) and cast onto the screen of a so-called Vidikon (television eye). This scans the picture in lines, the varying light intensity being transformed into successive current pulses. The logarithms of the pulses are formed and integrated by a computer and they can then be observed, for example as an extinction distribution curve on an oscillograph. The integrated voltage for each zone that has been separated in the pherogram is stored, recalled for measurement by a digital voltmeter, and printed out automatically. The result can be given directly in relative percentage. Figure 27 shows the principle of the procedure schematically.

In this way analytical data on the protein composition of, for example, serum samples can be obtained at short time intervals of 10 min, if the evaluation is done with UV radiation (280 mμ). The use of a Vidikon sensitive to the ultraviolet allows the bands of proteins or other UV absorbers to be made directly visible by the television process.

K. HANNIG

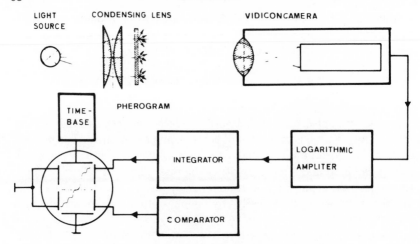

Fig. 27. Electronic densitometer (diagram).

References

1. W. Grassmann and K. Hannig, Deutsches Bundespatent 805399 (1949); *Angew. Chem.*, **62**, 170 (1950); *Ber. Physiol;* **139**, 220 (1950); K. Hannig, Dissertation, University of Darmstadt, 1953.
2. H. Svensson and I. Brattsten, *Arkiv Kemi,* **1**, 401 (1949).
3. S. Winsten, H. Friedman, and E. Schwarz, *Anal. Biochem.*, **6**(5), 404 (1963); H. Friedman, *Sci. Tools,* **10**, 7 (1963).
4. W. Grassmann and K. Hannig, *Naturwissenschaften,* **37**, 397 (1950); *Z. Physiol. Chem.*, **292**, 32 (1953); H. H. Strain and J. C. Sullivan, *Anal. Chem.*, **23**, 816 (1951); A. Karler, *Anal. Chem.*, **31**, 848 (1959); H. Jonas and V. Charlottesville, *J. Lab. Clin. Med.*, **49**, 135 (1957); E. S. Holdsworth, *Biochem. J.*, **59**, 340 (1955).
5. K. Hannig, *Clin. Chim. Acta,* **3**, 10 (1958); *Z. Physiol. Chem.*, **311**, 63 (1958).
6. E. L. Durrum, *J. Am. Chem. Soc.*, **73**, 4875 (1951).
7. I. Brattsten and A. Nilsson, *Arkiv. Kemi,* **3**, 337 (1951).
8. K. Hannig, *Z. Anal. Chem.*, **181**, 244 (1961).
9. Ch. Fröhlich, *Klin. Wochschr.*, **45**, 461 (1967).
10. W. Seitz and D. Eberhagen, *Z. Klin. Chem.*, **4**, 22 (1966).
11. E. Bidwell, G. W. F. Dike, and K. W. E. Denson, *Brit. J. Haematol.*, **12**, 583 (1966).
12. E. Waldschmidt-Leitz and H. Kling, *Z. Physiol. Chem.*, **346**, 17 (1966).
13. W. G. Jaffé and K. Hannig, *Arch. Biochem. Biophys.*, **109**, 80 (1965).
14. R. L. M. Synge, *Biochem. J.*, **65**, 266 (1957); A. C. Jennings, A. Pusztai, R. L. M. Synge, and W. B. Watt, *J. Sci. Fd. Agric.*, **19**, 203 (1968).
15. S. Sarkar, *Z. Naturforsch.*, **21b**, 1202 (1966).
16. E. Sulkowski and M. Laskowski, Sr., *Anal. Biochem.*, **20**, 94 (1967).
17. H. Hörmann and T. Fuji, *Z. Physiol. Chem.*, **328**, 65 (1962).
18. W. Grassmann, L. Strauch, and A. Nordwig, *Z. Physiol. Chem.*, **332**, 325 (1963).

19. E. Mehl and J. Jatzkewitz, *Z. Physiol. Chem.*, **339**, 260 (1964).
20. A. Nordwig and W. F. Jahn, *Z. Physiol. Chem.*, **345**, 284 (1966); *European J. Biochem.*, **3**, 519 (1968).
21. T. Gürtner, Dissertation, University of Munich, 1966.
22. O. Wieland, private communication.
23. F. Lynen, private communication.
24. Worthington Biochemical Corporation, Freehold, N. J., Reviews 4–67 (1967).
25. C. J. François and M. J. Glimcher, *Biochim. Biophys. Acta*, **133**, 91 (1967); *Biochem. J.*, **102**, 148 (1967).
26. K. Bräumer and K. Kühn, Conf. Biochimie et Physiologie du Tissu Conjonctif, E. Compte, Lyon, 1965, p. 69.
27. T. A. Mashburn, Jr., and P. Hoffman, *Anal. Biochem.*, **16**, 267 (1966).
28. G. Braunitzer, G. Hobom, and K. Hannig, *Z. Physiol. Chem.*, **338**, 276, 278 (1964).
29. K. Hannig, *Z. Physiol. Chem.*, **338**, 211 (1964).
30. M. Ganser, K. Hannig, W. F. Krüsmann, G. Pascher, and G. Ruhenstroth-Bauer, *Klin. Wochenschr.*, **46**, 809 (1968).
31. K. Hannig and W. F. Krüsmann, *Z. Physiol. Chem.*, **349**, 161 (1968).
32. K. Hannig and H. Wrba, *Z. Naturforsch.*, **19b**, 860 (1964).
33. A. Schweiger and K. Hannig, *Z. Physiol. Chem.*, **348**, 1005 (1967).
34. J. H. Matthaei, H. P. Voigt, G. Heller, R. Neth, G. Schöch, H. Kübler, F. Amelunxen, G. Sander, and A. Parmeggiani, *Cold Spring Harbor Symp. Quant. Biol.* **31**; *The Genetic Code, June 2–9, 1966*, p. 25.
35. W. Klofat and K. Hannig, *Z. Physiol. Chem.*, **348**, 739, 1332 (1967).
36. A. Strickler, A. Kaplan, and E. Vigh, *Microchem. J.*, **10**, 529 (1966); A. Strickler, *Separation Sci.*, **2**(3), 335 (1967).
37. A. Kolin, *Proc. Natl. Acad. Sci. U.S.*, **46**, 509 (1960); **51**, 1110 (1964); *J. Chromatography*, **26**, 164 (1967).

The Use of Gradients of Colloidal Silica for the Separation of Cells and Subcellular Particles

HÅKAN PERTOFT AND TORVARD C. LAURENT

Department of Medical Chemistry, University of Uppsala, Uppsala, Sweden

INTRODUCTION

In this paper a review will be given of work on silica gradients carried out in our laboratory and a number of others in Sweden. We are grateful to our colleagues and collaborators who have allowed us to mention their work before official publication.

The work originated from our experiments on the effects of various polymers, especially polysaccharides, on the sedimentation rates of particles and macromolecules (1–3). We had intended using the sieving effect of the polymers for particle separations on a preparative scale and for this needed a stabilizing gradient, in which the polymers could be dissolved. Many of the materials which have been used, e.g., CsCl, sucrose, albumin, Ficoll, and other polymers, have various draw-

* Supported by grants from the Swedish Medical Research Council (B68-13X-4-04C), the Swedish Cancer Society, and Knut och Alice Wallenbergs Stiftelse.

71

backs. The criteria for such a material, at least in cell separations, are:

1. The material should be able to form solutions of high density.
2. The solutions should have a low viscosity.
3. The solutions should have a low osmotic pressure.
4. It should be possible to work at physiological pH and ionic strength.
5. The gradient material should be easily removed from the material separated in the gradient.
6. The gradient material should not react with the material being studied.

There are also other criteria which could be mentioned, e.g., that the material should not be prohibitively expensive and that it should not interfere with the various analytical techniques used in the work.

In the search for the ideal compound, we tested colloidal silica. The properties of this material are in itself so interesting that we have been working on it for a couple of years and have rather deviated from the original approach. A few reports on the use of colloidal silica for preparative biological work have been published earlier. Mateyko and Kopac separated various types of cells on "cushions" of colloidal silica (4), Hayek and Tipton prepared liver cells (5), and Juhos separated bacteria and bacteriophages (6).

II. GENERAL PROPERTIES OF COLLOIDAL SILICA

An extensive review of the chemistry of colloidal silica has been given by Iler (7). It is sold, e.g., by DuPont under the trade name Ludox in solutions of up to 40% concentration, corresponding to a density of 1.30 g/ml. As a result of the spherical shape of the particles, the suspensions have low viscosities even at high concentrations. Ludox HS has a particle diameter of 80–250 Å (average 150 Å) and Ludox SM has particles of 50–150 Å diameter (average 70 Å) (1,8,9). An electron-microscopic picture of Ludox HS is shown in Figure 1. The chemical structure of the particles is shown in Figure 2.

Ludox is supplied as an aqueous suspension with a pH in the range of 8.3–9.8. It is very stable at alkaline and acid pH and can be neutralized in the presence of $0.2N$ salt and lower without any appreciable decrease in stability. It is thus possible to work at physiological pH and ionic strength. It can also be autoclaved.

If a suspension of Ludox is centrifuged in a preparative ultracentrifuge, either in a swing-out head or preferably in an angle-head rotor,

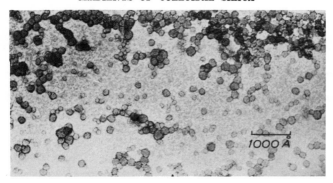

Fig. 1. Electron microscopy of Ludox HS particles, negatively contrasted with 1% uranyl acetate at pH 4.6. [Taken from H. Pertoft et al., *Virology*, **33**, 185 (1967)].

a density gradient is formed in the centrifuge tube (10). This is due to the polydispersity in the size of the colloidal silica particles which therefore sediment at different rates (Fig. 3). Examples of such density gradients are demonstrated in Figure 4. If a polymer is mixed with the silica suspension before the centrifugation, one obtains closer to linear gradients (Fig. 5) since the molecular-sieve effect of the polymer retards the transport of the large particles more than the small ones (1–3).

III. SEPARATION OF CELLS

It was of immediate interest to establish whether the density gradients formed by colloidal silica could be employed for the separation of various cells. The technique has therefore been applied to several systems. The main stages in this work are: (*1*) dispersion of the cells to be separated; (*2*) choice of conditions for optimal resolution in the density centrifugation; (*3*) removal of gradient material from the cells;

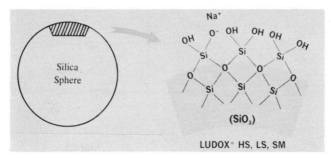

Fig. 2. Demonstration of the chemical structure of colloidal silica. (Reproduced from DuPont product information bulletin: Ludox, Colloidal silica.)

A   B

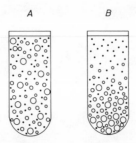

Fig. 3. Visualization of the distribution of colloidal silica particles in a centrifuge tube before and after high speed centrifugation.

(4) check on the recovery and intactness of the cells after separation. The last stage presents considerable difficulties as one can only investigate a few of the cellular functions.

A. Blood cells (11,12)

Heparinized blood was mixed (3:1) with a suspending medium, which was a modified Krebs-Ringer solution containing sodium acetate, 1% gelatine, and the dipotassium salt of 2-naphthol-6,8-disulfonic acid (G-acid). These components have been found by other investigators to inhibit cell aggregation.

Ludox HS was neutralized with hydrochloric acid and mixed with polyvinylpyrrolidone (PVP), mol wt=40,000, and sodium chloride to

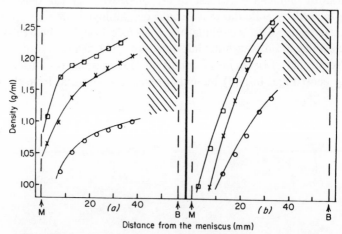

Fig. 4. Density gradients generated in Ludox HS after centrifugation for 30 min (a) and 60 min (b) at 35,000 rpm (○) 15% Ludox; (×) 24% Ludox; and (□) 30% Ludox. [Taken from H. Pertoft, *Biochim. Biophys. Acta,* **126,** 594 (1966).]

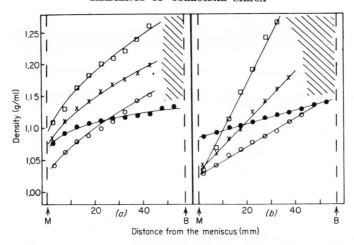

Fig. 5. Density gradients generated in Ludox HS in the presence of dextran (mol wt 2×10^6) during centrifugation for 30 min (a) and 60 min (b) at 35,000 rpm (○) 15% Ludox and 2% dextran; (✕) 24% Ludox; and 2% dextran; (□) 30% Ludox and 2% dextran; and (●) 15% Ludox and 10% dextran. [Taken from H. Pertoft, *Biochim. Biophys. Acta*, **126**, 594 (1966).]

give a final pH of 7.5; the Ludox concentration was 16.7% (w/v) (density 1.10 g/ml); the PVP concentration was 2.5 or 5%; the sodium chloride concentration was $0.085M$; and the osmolality physiological (310 mosm). The suspension was centrifuged in a Spinco Model L ultracentrifuge either in rotor 40.2 at 35,000 rpm for 20 min or in rotor 21 at 15,000 rpm for 80 min, after which suitable gradients for blood cell separations had formed. The volumes in the tubes in the two runs were 6.5 and 95 ml, respectively. A certain volume was removed from the bottom of each tube to allow an upper layer of 0.9 or 20 ml, respectively, of the blood samples to be introduced. The tubes were then centrifuged at 800g in an ordinary laboratory centrifuge with a swing-out head for 50 min. An example of the fractionation of blood cells is shown in Figure 6. There are four quite distinct bands corresponding to red blood cells at a density of 1.09–1.10, polymorphonuclear cells at 1.07–1.085, mononuclear cells at 1.050–1.065, and thrombocytes at 1.04–1.05.

Knowing at which densities various cells are banding, one can simplify the technique and use three density cushions instead of one as used by Mateyko and Kopac for other kinds of cells. If Ludox suspensions of densities 1.090, 1.068, and 1.050 are layered on top of each other, the various cell fractions can be recovered at the interfaces between the solutions. Such an experiment is demonstrated in Figure 7.

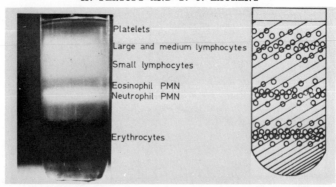

Fig. 6. Separation of blood cells on a 95-ml gradient of Ludox–polyvinyl-pyrrolidone. The experimental result has also been outlined in the sketch. The platelets are not clearly visible in the figure. [Part of the figure taken from H. Pertoft et al., *Exptl. Cell Res.*, **50,** 355 (1968).]

The centrifuge tubes may be emptied in different ways, and a number of devices have been published. A very simple method, which we have found useful, is demonstrated in Figure 8. The various cell fractions recovered were washed with physiological saline for removal of the silica.

Differential counts were made on each fraction, and the distribution of the various cell types is shown in Figure 9 and 10. There is some overlap between the thrombocytes and the mononuclear cells as well as between the polymorphonuclear cells and the red blood cells. However, each species may be obtained almost pure by taking narrower fractions. Differential cell counts on the white blood cells (Fig. 10) show that monocytes form a band at a density of 1.055, large and

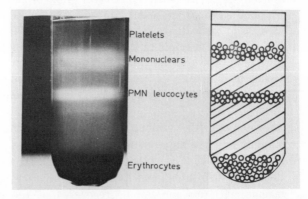

Fig. 7. Separation of blood cells with the aid of density cushions. [Part of the figure from H. Pertoft et al., *Exptl. Cell Res.*, **50,** 355 (1968).]

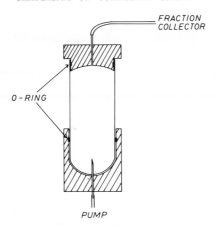

Fig. 8. Device for fractionation of the colloidal silica gradients. Forty per cent silica is pumped with a peristaltic pump into the tube from the bottom and this displaces the gradient which may be collected in fractions from the top. The important feature is the insertion of the O-rings, which form a tight fit between the centrifuge tube and cup and the top insertion and tube respectively. At the start of the operation, the space between the cup and the tube is filled with a 40% silica solution.

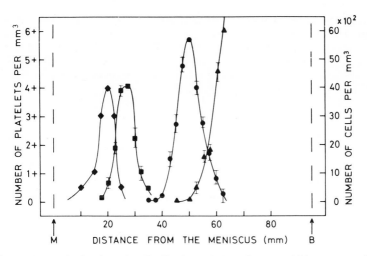

Fig. 9. A graph showing the distribution of thrombocytes (♦); mononuclear cells (■); polymorphonuclear cells (●); and red blood cells (▲); from 15 ml of blood separated on a 95-ml Ludox–polyvinylpyrrolidone gradient. [Taken from H. Pertoft et al., *Exptl. Cell Res., 50,* 355 (1968).]

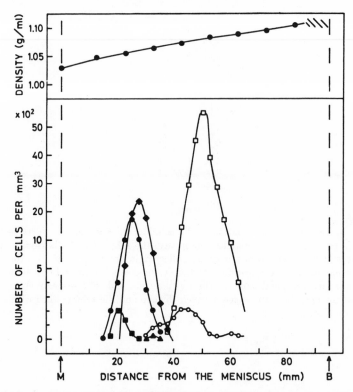

Fig. 10. A graph showing the distribution of white blood cells from 15 ml of blood separated on a 95-ml Ludox–polyvinylpyrrolidone gradient. Monocytes (■); large and medium size lymphocytes (●); small lymphocytes (◆); basophilic leucocytes (▲); eosinophilic leucocytes (○); and neutrophilic leucocytes (□). The density gradient is shown in the upper part of the figure. [Taken from H. Pertoft et al., *Exptl. Cell Res.*, **50**, 355 (1968).]

medium-sized lymphocytes at 1.058, and small lymphocytes at 1.063. The basophilic leucocytes form a diffuse band at an approximate density of 1.067, the eosinophilic a broad band at approximately 1.07, and the neutrophilic a single zone at 1.082.

The recovery of the various white blood cells is given in Table I and is low only for the monocytes. Various tests on the viability of the white blood cells were performed. Ninety-eight to ninety-nine per cent accumulated fluoresceindiacetate and only 1–2% took up trypan blue, which is an indication of a high survival rate. The incorporation of thymidine into lymphocytes after stimulation with phytohemagglutinin indicated an intact DNA synthesis. The latter took place, however, only if there was an SH-reagent present in the medium, e.g.,

TABLE I

Recovery of White Blood Cells after Centrifugation in 95-ml Gradient [a]

Cellular components	Total number of cells in whole blood ($\times 10^6$)	Number of cells after separation ($\times 10^6$)	Yield (%)
White blood cells	136	108	80
Neutrophilic leucocytes	81	68	84
Eosinophilic leucocytes	4.9	4.4	90
Lymphocytes	45	35	78
Monocytes	5.4	1.2	22

[a] The 95-ml gradient was collected in 2.7-ml fractions and four cell counts, and two differential counts were made on each fraction. Six counts were made on the original blood. The mean values of the counts are given in the Table. The yield is expressed as the total number of cells recovered in the gradient as a percentage of the number of cells in the original blood sample. [Taken from H. Pertoft et al., *Exptl. Cell Res.*, **50**, 355 (1968).]

glutathione or Cleland's reagent. The role of the SH-reagent will be discussed below. White blood cells from leukemic patients can be purified to a high degree by the silica gradient technique. Contaminating thrombocytes can conveniently be removed in advance in a fibrin clot (13).

B. Liver Cells (14)

The dispersion of liver cells to give a suspension of single cells is generally achieved by mechanical treatment, enzymes, or chelating agents (for a review see refs. 15 and 16). The following technique was adopted for our experiments. Rat livers were first perfused *in situ* with physiological saline and then perfused at 37°C with a solution containing physiological saline, 0.027M sodium citrate, and 0.5% glucose at pH 6.5. In a special homogenizer (15) 5 g of wet liver were homogenized at room temperature in 50 ml of horse serum or 12 (or 17)% polyethyleneglycol (PEG) with a molecular weight of 1500 (or 4000).

Preformed gradients of silica were obtained by centrifuging suspensions containing 95 ml of 17.1% (w/v) Ludox HS and 5% of PEG (mol wt 4000) in 0.094M sodium chloride at pH 7.5 for 40 min at 10,000 rpm using rotor 21. Approximately 40×10^6 liver cells suspended in 10 ml of physiological saline were layered on top of the gradient and the tubes were spun in a swing-out head at 800*g* for 30–40 min.

The separation of the liver cells is shown in Figure 11. There are several visible bands but the resolution between them is not high, as revealed by cell counts on the different fractions (Fig. 12). Fraction A seems to contain only a few cells and consists of subcellular particles presumably from disintegrated cells. Fractions B, C, and D contain large oval cells with large nuclei and have densities in the range 1.095–1.105. At a density of approximately 1.11, there is a band (E), which contains cells showing a greater tendency to aggregate. The cells have more elongated triangular shape and a darker nucleus. When india ink was injected in the animal 48 hr before it was sacrificed, many of these cells contained dark inclusions.

Mateyko and Kopac (4) centrifuged liver cells and found at least two different populations of cells, one lighter, containing the liver cells proper, and one heavier, containing fibrous and Kupffer cells. Our results seem to be in agreement with this observation.

A frequent problem is the contamination of liver cells by red cells, e.g., in a liver biopsy. In this case, a cushion technique has been found most useful. A cushion with Ludox HS and PEG as above and a density of 1.07 completely separates human liver cells from red blood cells (17).

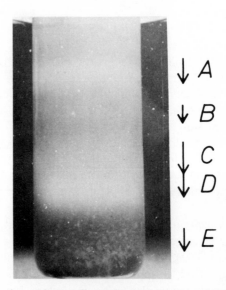

Fig. 11. The separation of liver cells on a 95-ml gradient of Ludox–polyethylen-glycol.

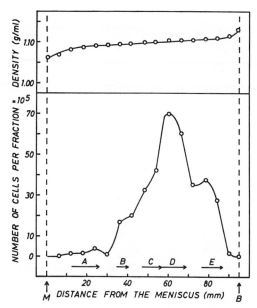

Fig. 12. A graph showing the distribution of 38.5×10^6 liver cells in a gradient similar to that in Figure 10. The number of cells in each 7-ml fraction was counted. Subcellular particles were found on the top of the gradient and in Fraction A, while Fractions B–E contained essentially whole cells. The density gradient is shown in the upper part of the figure.

C. Miscellaneous Cells

It is possible to separate the cellular components of a number of different systems. Cells from peritoneal fluid of guinea pig could be fractionated into macrophages, eosinophilic leucocytes, and red blood cells (18). Bone marrow cells may be fractionated in a number of bands (19). Skin fibroblasts from cell cultures are well separated from lymphocytes (20). Figure 13 shows a typical experiment where human fibroblasts and lymphocytes have been mixed with 5.5% (w/v) of Ludox HS and 5% PEG (mol wt 4000) and 0.094M sodium chloride. The mixture has been centrifuged at 20,000g for 30 min. The lymphocytes banded at a density of 1.06 and the fibroblasts at 1.03 g/ml. The latter have been washed in 17% PEG (mol wt 4000) and then in Eagle's solution and thereafter grown in tissue culture.

IV. EXPERIMENTS WITH VIRUSES

The first experiments were carried out with tobacco mosaic virus (TMV), turnip yellow mosaic virus (TYMV), polio- and adenovirus

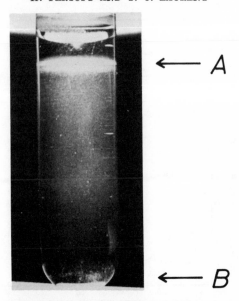

Fig. 13. Separation of 10^6 skin fibroblasts (A) from 20×10^6 lymphocytes (B) in a 4-ml Ludox–polyethylene glycol gradient. Density gradient 1.025–1.065. (Published with permission from H. Pertoft, L. Philipson, and J. Pontén.)

(8). Of these the TYMV particle is evidently too small to form a band in a silica gradient. The sedimentation rate of the virus is of the same order as that of the silica particles. The experiment with TYMV affords a good estimate of the smallest particle size that can be investigated using the commercial silica colloids described here.

In the first studies (8) the viruses were mixed with Ludox and the mixture was then centrifuged in angle head rotors. The pH in the solution was adjusted to 7.5–8, but no extra salt or polymer was added. Sometimes EDTA ($10^{-3}M$) and Cleland's reagent ($10^{-2}M$) were included. During the runs, the gradients were constantly changing in the tubes such that the viruses, which layered at their hydrated density levels steadily moved down the tube. This is demonstrated for TMV in Figure 14. The density level at which TMV moved was 1.065. Also polio- and adenovirus accumulated at the top of the gradient after centrifugation for short periods and then sedimented as very sharp bands at density levels of 1.19 and 1.23, respectively.

It is more difficult to separate viruses from the silica than cells. A number of techniques have been tested including electrophoresis, gel chromatography, etc. The most effective turned out to be precipitation of the silica with polyvalent amines such as spermin and spermidine.

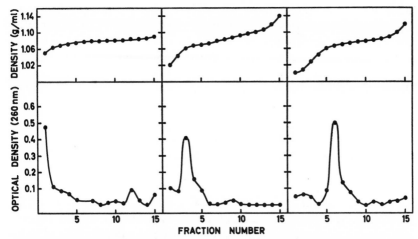

Fig. 14. Centrifugation of TMV in Ludox SM (density 1.09) at approximately 100,000g for 10, 30, and 60 min, respectively. The tops of the tubes are to the left of the figures. The density gradients in the tubes are indicated in the upper set of diagrams. At the beginning of the run, the TMV concentrates at the meniscus but subsequently moves down through the tube as the density gradient changes. [Taken from H. Pertoft et al., *Virology*, **33**, 185 (1967).]

Electron-microscopic pictures of TMV before and after removal of colloidal silica with spermidine shows that the method is very efficient (Fig. 15). Experiments with radioactive polio- and adenovirus showed that the recovery of the virus was quite satisfactory provided that the

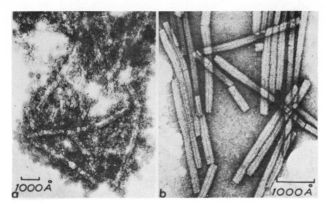

Fig. 15. (*a*) Sample from the zone containing TMV after centrifugation for 60 minutes at 100,000g as described in Figure 14. (*b*) The same sample after precipitation of the Ludox with spermidine and removal of the precipitate by centrifugation at 10,000g for 30 min. [Taken from H. Pertoft et al., *Virology*, **33**, 185 (1967).]

silica was precipitated under the correct ionic conditions. The precipitation of silica with divalent amines also afforded full recovery of the infectivity (see Table II).

The experiments cited above clearly show that centrifugation in colloidal silica may be used for purification of viruses. Figure 16 shows the purification of poliovirus (20). A partly purified ^{32}P-labeled virus suspension was layered over a suspension of 17.1% (w/v) of Ludox HS containing 5% PEG (mol wt 4000) and 0.094M sodium chloride. No chelator or SH-reagent was present. The solution was centrifuged for 30 min at 100,000g. Fractions were collected and diluted in 0.05M phosphate buffer, pH 7.2, in 0.15M sodium chloride. The Ludox was then precipitated and removed by low speed contrifugation. The supernatants were analyzed for radioactivity and infectivity. The purification is the same as that obtained using a CsCl gradient. Ludox–PEG gradients should be especially useful for the purification of large viruses for which CsCl centrifugation is less satisfactory.

V. OTHER SUBCELLULAR PARTICLES

Although the method has not been explored extensively, there are indications that centrifugation in colloidal silica may be useful for the preparation of various cellular organelles.

Ronquist has used the technique to prepare erythrocyte membranes (21). A purified membrane fraction obtained from human erythrocytes resulted in a band at a density of 1.08. This band was well defined and separated from hemoglobin-containing structures and other proteins (Fig. 17). The membranes prepared in this way showed the characteristic double-layer structure in the electron microscope.

TABLE II

Recovery of Polio- and Adenovirus Infectivity after Precipitation of the Silica

	Poliovirus (PFU/ml) after dilution in		Adenovirus (PFU/ml) after dilution in	
Precipitating amine	PBS–EDTA[a]	0.5M NaCl–EDTA[a]	PBS–EDTA[a]	0.5M NaCl–EDTA[a]
Spermidine HCl at $10^{-3}M$	2.2×10^6	3.0×10^6	5.2×10^6	4.2×10^7
None	2.6×10^6	2.8×10^6	3.6×10^7	4.1×10^7

[a] PBS denotes 0.15M NaCl, 0.02M phosphate buffer pH 7.2. The final concentration of EDTA was $10^{-3}M$. [Taken from H. Pertoft et al., *Virology*, **33**, 185 (1967).]

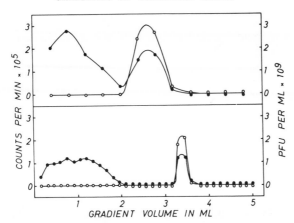

Fig. 16. A sample of 1 ml of Ecteola purified ^{32}P-labeled polio virus suspension centrifuged in a Ludox–polyethylene glycol gradient gives a ^{32}P-labeled peak (●) with associated infectivity (○) which is well separated from other ^{32}P-labeled materials. For comparison a similar experiment in a preformed CsCl-gradient with a density gradient of 1.2–1.5, run for 5 hr at 100,000g is shown. The degree of purification is approximately the same in the two runs. (Published with permission from H. Pertoft, L. Philipson, and J. Pontén.)

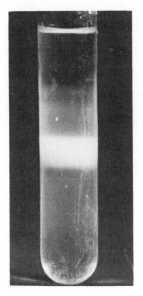

Fig. 17. Banding of erythrocyte membranes in a 6.5-ml gradient of 20% (w/v) of Ludox HS obtained after centrifugation at 100,000g for 20 min in an angle head rotor (Spinco Model 40.2). (Published with permission from G. Ronquist.)

Further phosphoglycerate kinase activity and glyceraldehyde-phosphate dehydrogenase activity were still present, the latter, however, only after addition of SH-reagents.

Olsson (22) has centrifuged cytoplasmic granules from leucocytes in colloidal silica. The granule fraction was incorporated in a Ludox HS solution with a density of 1.23 and at physiological pH and osmolality. The solution also contained 3% dextran (mol wt 40,000) and glutathione. The mixture was centrifuged at 26,000g for 40 min, and the fractions obtained from the gradient were analyzed enzymatically (Fig. 18). All the alkaline phosphatase activity resided at the top of the gradient, while all the acid phosphatase, β-glucuronidase, and β-galactosidase activity was found near the bottom. Electron-microscopic analyses were made on the bottom fractions after they had been washed twice with sucrose solutions. The pictures showed an intact granula fraction contaminated with some silica.

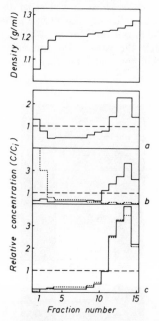

Fig. 18. Purification of cytoplasmic granules from leucocytes in a Ludox gradient. The diagram shows the distribution of (a) protein; (b) phosphatases (— acid, - - - - alkaline); and (c) – β-galactosidase, - - - - β-glucuronidase; in the gradient after the run and is expressed as C/C_i, where C is the measured concentration and C_i the concentration of the material had it been homogeneously distributed over the whole gradient. The recovery of protein and enzymes was nearly quantitative. The density gradient in the tube is indicated in the upper diagram. (Published with permission from I. Olsson.)

Finally it should be mentioned that preliminary experiments in our laboratory with silica gradients in the zonal centrifuge (23) show that homogenates of liver cells can be banded in a number of very sharp fractions. The fractions have not yet been identified.

VI. THE EFFECT OF SILICA COLLOIDS ON BIOLOGICAL ACTIVITY

It is well known that silica particles have toxic effects (24). Several authors have shown that silica causes hemolysis (25). It has also been found that macrophages engulf silica particles, leading to cytolysis (26). The reactions are most probably due to reactions between silica and the cell surfaces.

The toxic reactions of silica may, however, be inhibited by various polymers. Even very dilute solutions of plasma completely inhibit the hemolytic effect (25), and aluminum-coated silica and silica in the presence of polyvinylpyridine-N-oxide inhibits the cytolysis of macrophages (26). The polymers presumably coat the silica particles (7,24). Preliminary experiments in our laboratory, involving conductivity and pH measurements, vapor pressure measurements, and chemical analysis of free PEG in mixtures of Ludox and PEG indicate a definite binding between the polymer and the silica.

Although the addition of polymers in our experiments was primarily aimed at influencing the gradient formation (10), it was subsequently realized that they had a very beneficial effect on the biological activities of the materials studied. Only the TMV and TYMV viruses retained their biological activities in the absence of polymers or SH-reagents.

In several experiments the presence of thiol reagents was essential. In the absence of such a reagent lymphocytes failed to incorporate thymidine, and glyceraldehyde-phosphate dehydrogenase lost its activity. One of the effects of silica is therefore presumably that it catalyzes the oxidation of SH-groups. When animal viruses were examined, it was also found necessary to include a chelating agent in the solution. Metal analyses showed that Ludox contains 0.01% titanium, 0.015% iron, and 0.015% magnesium, and other heavy metals in trace amounts (20). The chelator presumably binds these impurities. It is interesting, however, that adeno- and poliovirus retain their infectivities in Ludox in the presence of polyethylene glycol without the addition of chelator and sulfhydryl reagents. The polymer thus seems to coat the reactive sites on the silica particles (20). Polyethylene glycol in the molecular weight range 1500–4000 was most effective in this respect.

VII. THE EXCLUSION EFFECT

It is obvious that the banding in the silica gradients is determined by density as the viruses and cells always layer at the same density, independent of centrifugation time. There are, however, some observations in connection with the recorded apparent densities of the particles. When various polystyrene particles of different sizes were studied in the same gradient, the bands formed in order of particle size. The largest particles were found to have the largest apparent densities (Fig. 19) (10) even though they are made of the same material and ought to have approximately the same absolute densities.

TMV and other viruses seem to have a much lower density than that observed in other experiments (Table III). Furthermore, TMV banded at different densities depending on the particle size of the silica colloid. The larger the particle size, the lower the apparent density of TMV (8).

The phenomenon can be explained in terms of an exclusion effect (27). The silica particles are excluded from a certain volume around the viruses and the polystyrene particles and this volume can be regarded as the hydrated volume of the banded substance. It varies

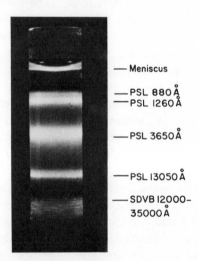

Fig. 19. Banding of four samples of polystyrene latex(PSL) and one styrene–divinyl benzene copolymer latex (SDVB) with different particle diameters in a 6.5-ml Ludox HS gradient having a density range from 1.052 to 1.075 g/ml. [Taken from H. Pertoft, *Biochim. Biophys. Acta*, **126**, 594 (1966).]

TABLE III

Bouyant Densities of Three Viruses in Solutions of Colloidal Silica and Cesium Chloride

Virus	Density in silica (g/ml)	Density in CsCl (g/ml)
TMV	1.065	1.32
Adenovirus	1.23	1.34
Poliovirus	1.19[a]	1.32

[a] When 5% PEG, molecular weight 4000, was included in the medium, the polio virus had a density of 1.08 (compare experiment in Fig. 16). [Table taken from H. Pertoft et al., *Virology*, **33**, 185 (1967).]

naturally with the size of the silica particles, and it increases with decreasing size and increasing asymmetry of the particles studied. The apparent density of a substance in a silica gradient is thus not only dependent on its absolute density but also on its size and shape.

VIII. CONCLUDING REMARKS

We hope that it is clear from our presentation that the technique of centrifuging biological materials in colloidal silica gradients cannot yet be regarded as a standard technique. There are too many unknown factors, especially regarding the effects of silica on the biological activity of various materials. It is, however, our conviction that the advantages of this method over others are in many respects so great that the technique demands a thorough exploration. The following advantages will be enumerated: (*1*) The colloidal silica suspensions form self generating density gradients in the ultracentrifuge over a very wide density range (1–1.45 g/ml); (*2*) The suspensions have very low viscosities and colloid osmotic pressures and can be adjusted to physiological pH and ionic strength; (*3*) centrifugation times are very short and angle head rotors have been used with good results; (*4*) the experiments can be made on widely different scales, and the low price of colloidal silica allows large scale work; (*5*) for particles within the same size range as the silica particles, it is possible to take advantage of the exclusion effect; (*6*) commercial Ludox has been used without further purification, and the additions of polymers or SH-reagents have inhibited interaction between the biological material and the silica sol; (*7*) cells can be washed free from silica whereas viruses are best recovered by precipitation of the silicas. There is as yet no good standard method for separating other subcellular particles from the silica colloid.

90

H. PERTOFT AND T. C. LAURENT

With the silica at present employed the technique is only applicable for particles with sedimentation values of more than approximately 60S.

References

1. T. C. Laurent, I. Björk, A. Pietruszkiewicz, and H. Persson, *Biochim. Biophys. Acta*, **78**, 351 (1963).
2. T. C. Laurent and H. Persson, *Biochim. Biophys. Acta*, **78**, 360 (1963).
3. T. C. Laurent and H. Persson, *Biochim. Biophys. Acta*, **83**, 141 (1964).
4. G. M. Mateyko and M. J. Kopac, *Ann. N.Y. Acad. Sci.*, **105**, 219 (1963).
5. D. H. Hayek and S. R. Tipton, *J. Cellular Biol.*, **29**, 405 (1966).
6. E. Juhos, *J. Bacteriol.*, **91**, 1376 (1966).
7. R. K. Iler, *The Colloid Chemistry of Silica and Silicates*, Cornell University Press, Ithaca, New York, 1955.
8. H. Pertoft, L. Philipson, P. Oxelfelt, and S. Höglund, *Virology*, **33**, 185 (1967).
9. *Ludox Colloidal Silica;* product information bulletin, E. I. du Pont de Nemours & Co.
10. H. Pertoft, *Biochim. Biophys. Acta*, **126**, 594 (1966).
11. H. Pertoft, *Expl. Cell Res.*, **46**, 621 (1967).
12. H. Pertoft, O. Bäck, and K. Lindahl-Kiessling, *Expl. Cell Res.*, **50**, 355 (1968).
13. In collaboration with Dr. A. Killander, The Academic Hospital, Uppsala, Sweden.
14. H. Pertoft, to be published.
15. S. T. Jacob and P. M. Bhargava, *Expl. Cell Res.*, **27**, 453 (1962).
16. C. Rappaport and G. B. Howze, *Proc. Soc Exptl. Biol. Med.*, **121**, 1010 (1966).
17. In collaboration with Dr. R. Ekman, The Academic Hospital, Uppsala, Sweden.
18. In collaboration with Drs. U. Friberg and G. Rodenborg, Department of Histology, Karolinska Institutet, Stockholm.
19. I. Olsson and H. Pertoft, *Communication XXIV Med. Congress, Stockholm, 1967,* p. 103.
20. H. Pertoft, L. Philipson, and J. Pontén, to be published.
21. G. Ronquist, personal communication.
22. I. Olsson, *Exptl. Cell Res.* In press.
23. N. G. Andersson, *Methods of Biochem. Anal.*, **15**, 272 (1967).
24. T. Nash, A. C. Allison, and J. S. Harington, *Nature*, **210**, 259 (1966).
25. J. D. Harley and J. Margolis, *Nature*, **189**, 1010 (1961).
26. A. C. Allison, J. S. Harington, and H. Birbeck, *J. Expl. Med.*, **124**, 141 (1966).
27. T. C. Laurent, in *The Chemical Physiology of Mucopolysaccharides*, G. Quintarelli, Ed., Little, Brown, Boston, 1968.

The Separation of Lymphocyte Populations on Glass Bead Columns *

KEN SHORTMAN

Walter and Eliza Hall Institute of Medical Research, Victoria, Australia

In this report two methods currently in use for obtaining pure preparations of small lymphocytes will be compared and contrasted. Both techniques use glass bead columns; however, here the similarity ends since the basis of the separation and the results obtained are quite different in the two cases.

I. ACTIVE ADHERENCE COLUMNS

The first technique is one now in common usage for separating lymphocytes, platelets, polymorphonuclear leucocytes, and monocytes from blood. The separation depends on the fact that all of these cells, except lymphocytes, show a strong tendency to adhere to solid surfaces such as siliconed or unsiliconed glass beads, glass wool, cotton wool, or nylon. The factors affecting the adhesiveness of these cells have been examined in detail by Garvin (2) and by Rabinowitz (6). To obtain adhesion of polymorphs and monocytes the following factors are essential:

1. A period of incubation, about 30 min at 37°. Adhesion is insignificant below 15°, when metabolic activity is low, or above 45° when the cells are inactivated.

* This is publication No. 1232 from the Walter & Eliza Hall Institute of Medical Research, Post Office, Royal Melbourne Hospital, Victoria, Australia. This work was supported by grants from the National Health and Medical Research Council, Canberra, and the Australian Research Grants Committee.

91

2. The presence of some heat-labile factor in fresh serum or plasma, and of both calcium and magnesium ions.

In general, adhesiveness is well correlated with the metabolic activity, the motility, and the phagocytic ability of these cells, and must itself be considered as an active process. The adhesiveness of platelets displays different requirements. It is largely independent of temperature and requires only a low concentration of either calcium or magnesium ions. Lacking a more precise description, we can attribute the attachment of platelets to their general "stickiness."

The initial step when working with whole blood is the removal of erythrocytes, since the columns do not separate these from lymphocytes. This is usually done by a sedimentation rate separation, which depends on the association of dense erythrocytes to form large rouleaux, which then sediment more rapidly than white cells. One can start with either defibrinated blood (in which case platelets are already removed) or with heparinized blood. Chelating agents such as ethylene diamine tetraacetate cannot be used as anticoagulants, since they bind the divalent ions necessary for later adherence to the column. Separation of mammalian blood can be effected by standing for 30 min after addition of dextran of sufficiently high molecular weight to enhance rouleau formation (see, e.g., Rabinowitz (6)). The supernatant fraction normally contains about half the original leucocytes, together with 1–4 times that number of contaminating erythrocytes. Separation of fowl blood is best carried out by repeated separation of the white cell buffy coat, using low centrifuge speeds and narrow tubes, according to the procedure of Szenberg (8). This gives a white cell preparation contaminated with 10–15% red cells.

The subsequent separation of blood elements according to their adherence characteristics is best exemplified by the technique of Rabinowitz (6), who used columns of siliconed beads about 200 μ in diameter. The beads are essential if phagocytic cells are to be recovered in good yield. However, if the aim is merely to remove adherent cells, leaving behind pure lymphocytes, mixed glass wool–glass bead columns are preferable, and columns of other material, such as glass wool, cotton wool, or nylon may be substituted. The leucocytes, concentrated if desired and suspended in isologous plasma or serum, are slowly run onto the top three-quarters of the column, and incubated at 37° for 30 min.

The successive elution of various blood elements from the column is shown in Figure 1, taken from Rabinowitz' paper (6). The nonadherent lymphocytes and contaminating erythrocytes are displaced from the column with fresh plasma or serum and largely appear within one

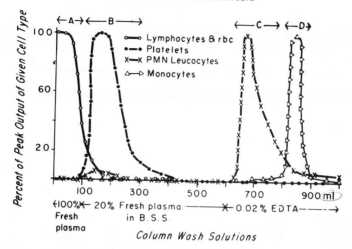

Fig. 1. The successive elution of human blood elements from an active adherence type glass bead column. The diagram is taken from Rabinowitz (6), whose paper should be consulted for a full account of the method.

column volume of effluent. The earlier part of the lymphocyte peak gives the greatest purity, the latter region having more platelets, phagocytic elements, and more erythrocytes (a significant proportion of which remain as rouleaux following dextran treatment, and are delayed by simple filtration effects). Further washing of the column with diluted plasma elutes the platelets. Note that a low number of polymorphs, probably inactive cells, are removed at this stage. The phagocytic elements can be eluted from the column by using 0.02% ethylene diamine tetraacetate in buffered, calcium- and maganesium-free saline. The polymorphs are eluted first, followed by monocytes, and with careful phase contrast monitoring these may be separated. The recoveries are around 60–70% for lymphocytes, 40% for polymorphs, and 20% for monocytes (6). In our hands this technique has given human small lymphocytes contaminated with about an equal number of erythrocytes but less than 2% of other blood elements. The cells are viable; the small lymphocytes readily develop into blast-like cells in culture when stimulated by phytohemagglutinin and monocytes develop in culture into fixed macrophages.

An important point should be noted here. The preparations are free of large lymphocytes only because the original preparation of adult human blood was free of this cell type. The method itself does not discriminate between large and small lymphocytes. Application of this type of glass bead column to mouse thoracic duct cells gave in our hands no discrimination between large, medium, and small lymphocytes (5). Likewise cotton wool columns have failed to significantly change the proportion of large to small lymphocytes when applied to chick buffy coat fraction (8,9).

II. SIZE FILTRATION COLUMNS

The second technique is one which was developed by us (7) in an attempt to separate cells by size. It also uses glass bead columns but differs in many respects from the Rabinowitz technique. Our work is done at 0–4° to eliminate any active adherence. The beads we currently use are from 50–90 μ diameter in contrast to the 200–300 μ size we use in the Rabinowitz technique. The smaller sized beads when packed provide a bed with a system of holes approaching the size range of the cells that interest us (6–15 μ diam). However, the column does not act as a simple filter since retention of cells by such columns varies markedly with the serum concentration, as shown in Figure 2. In the absence of serum almost all lymphocytes are retained by such a column, even after extensive washing. With increasing serum more lymphocytes pass through the column until a plateau of variable height is reached around 50% serum concentration. This plateau reflects the presence in the cell sample of a variable quantity of damaged cells, which are retained in the columns at all serum levels. It is possible to recover cells trapped by the column by gently resuspending

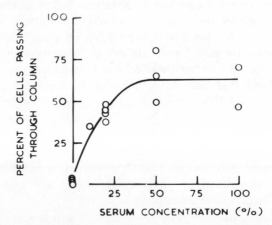

Fig. 2. The effect of serum concentration on the proportion of cells passing through a size filtration type glass bead column (7). 3×10^7 teased out rat lymph node cells were passed at 3 ml/hr through a 2 cm $\times$ 0.7 cm diameter column of 60–90 μ siliconed glass beads, at 4°C. The suspending medium was a balanced salt solution, pH 7.4, containing the noted levels of foetal calf serum.

the beads, allowing them to settle, and then taking the supernatant. However, cells will suffer some damage in this process.

In the 10–16% serum concentration range the column shows a selectivity for certain cell types. In a teased lymph node preparation the order of probability that a cell of a certain morphological class will be retained by the column is:

damaged cells ≫ large lymphocytes and blasts > medium lymphocytes and plasma cells > small lymphocytes > erythrocytes

Damaged cells are always trapped, but selectivity between the remaining cells is only obtained under a restricted range of conditions. Selectivity is lost (1) with high serum levels, (2) with beads larger than 90 μ, (3) with faster flow rates, (4) with excessive cell loads on the column, and (5) in the absence of divalent metals.

The removal of damaged cells, which come in all sizes can be attributed to their extreme "stickiness" and their tendency to form larger aggregates which are simply filtered out by the system. The remaining cells form a series whose probability of being trapped by the column is a simple function of size. It seems that the larger the cell the greater is its probability of being immobilized in the narrow channels of the column by some weak physical interaction with the bead surface.

We have made use of these observations in three ways (7). First, the columns may be used to remove damaged cells and debris from cell suspensions. Kovařík (3) has devised a similar technique. In this case, to avoid selecting between any normal cells, large beads (>100 μ), high serum levels (50–100%) and fast flow rates are used. A second procedure, carried out under conditions of optimum selectivity, is to separate a cell suspension into the column filtrate and the fraction recovered from the column bed, and then to resubject these fractions to further separation on fresh columns, in the manner of countercurrent distribution. This will produce a series of fractions showing a gradation in mean cell size, but the procedure is cumbersome, inefficient, and causes considerable damage. The third and most useful procedure is to aim only for the smallest cells, the small lymphocytes, which can be obtained in extremely pure state by continuing separation to select the 10% least adherent cells. The small lymphocytes will, of course, be contaminated with a few erythrocytes which are also enriched by this procedure, but these are at a low level in most tissues and can be ignored for most applications.

A typical small lymphocyte purification is as follows. A column 4 cm high by 3 cm diam is prepared from 50–70 μ diameter siliconed

glass beads. The beads are retained in the column by a small pad
of fine, siliconed glass wool, and the column is tapped to ensure efficient packing of the beads. The column is then equilibrated with the
cell suspension medium, 10% serum in a balanced salt solution, pH 7.4.
About 5×10^8 cells (for example, rat thoracic duct lymphocytes) are
suspended in 1.5 ml of medium and slowly run onto the column at 0–4°.
The upper few mm of the bead surface is then gently stirred to reduce
any nonspecific blockage in this region. The cells are then washed from
the column at a rate of 6–10 ml/hr, using the same medium. The first
75–90% of the eluted cells are concentrated and applied to a second
column in a similar manner. The final eluate represents the preparation of pure small lymphocytes, obtained with about 10% recovery.

This procedure must be changed slightly for other cell preparations.
For example, when using spleen cell suspensions, where a huge amount
of debris and damaged cells tend to block the column and reduce the
effective pore size, 60–90 μ beads, a 3-fold greater dilution of the
original suspension and 5- to 10-fold faster flow rates would be used.
For thymus cells, which are smaller than other lymphocytes, flow rates
slower than 5 ml/hr have to be employed. In all cases the parameters
are adjusted to give about 10% recovery of lymphocytes. Whole blood
cannot be used since the erythrocytes overload the column, and no
useful separation of white cells is obtained.

Examples of the separation attained are given in the Figures 3, 4,
and 5. If we make the problem as difficult as we can by using rat lymph
nodes 3.5 days after stimulation by a second injection of bacterial
flagella, our starting preparation of teased-out cells consists of small
lymphocytes, many damaged cells, (damaged during the teasing proc-

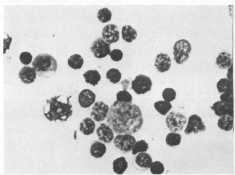

Fig. 3. This represents the starting material, an extensively teased suspension
from antigenically stimulated rat lymph nodes. The preparation shows small
lymphocytes, plasma cells, blasts and damaged cell material (7). Giemsa stain.
1000×.

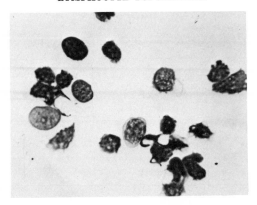

Fig. 4. This represents a damaged cell fraction that may be removed from the starting material by glass bead columns (7). Giemsa stain. 1000×.

ess), large, dividing blast-like cells, mature and immature plasma cells and a few macrophages (Fig. 3). We can clean up this preparation by using our technique for removal of damaged cells. The material eliminated in this process has been recovered from the columns and is shown in Figure 4. A small lymphocyte preparation consisting of >99.9% small lymphocytes, obtained from such a starting material, is given in Figure 5.

Some properties of these small lymphocyte preparations are given in Table I. The preparations are always very markedly reduced in damaged cells (7). Small lymphocytes purified from rat thoracic duct lose none of their ability to incorporate tritiated uridine into RNA (J. Mitchell, personal communication). However, there is always a very marked reduction (70-fold) in cells engaged in DNA synthesis,

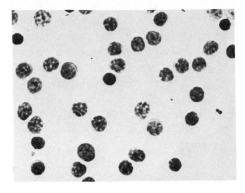

Fig. 5. A typical small lymphocyte preparation obtained by "filtering" with fine glass bead columns until only 10% of the cells remain (7). Giemsa stain. 1000×.

TABLE I

Properties of Purified Small Lymphocytes [a]

		Total cells active, %	
Activity assayed	Source of cells	Original suspension	Purified small lymphocytes
Damaged cells	Rat lymph nodes	38	5
RNA synthesis	Rat thoracic duct	85	88
DNA synthesis	Rat mesenteric lymph node	1.4	0.02

[a] Some properties of small lymphocyte preparations purified by size filtration on fine glass beads. Damaged cells were determined by Eosin uptake tests (7). RNA synthesis was determined by autoradiography after incubation *in vitro* with tritiated uridine (J. Mitchell, personal communication). DNA synthesis was determined by autoradiography of cells labeled by injection of tritiated thymidine into animals 2 hr prior to removal of nodes and cell separation (7); similar results were obtained by *in vitro* studies pre- and postcolumn purification (J. Mitchell, personal communication).

as judged by the uptake of tritiated thymidine *in vivo* (7) or *in vitro* (J. Mitchell, personal communication). Depending on rather arbitrary criteria, some of these purified small lymphocytes might be classed as medium lymphocytes; however, the essential point is that we have largely eliminated DNA synthesizing, dividing cells, leaving behind a population of mature lymphocytes.

The purification of small lymphocytes from fowl blood (8) serves as an example of the changes in size distribution of the column lymphocyte populations after separation by both techniques. Lymphocytes were first purified from chick blood (by Dr. A. Szenberg) by isolating the buffy coat fraction and then passing this through a cotton wool column to remove the adherent cells. This gives a preparation consisting only of lymphocytes and a negligible proportion of red cells, but the ratio of large to medium to small is not significantly changed. To separate the small from the medium and large cells we applied the small glass bead filtration technique. The Coulter Counter size range distribution of cells before and after filtration through the columns is shown in Figure 6. Since small lymphocytes are the dominant cell type, composing about 90% of our starting preparation, we cannot, of course, expect impressive purification factors; rather, the method should be regarded as a way of depleting the population of active dividing lymphocytes. The curves show a small enrichment of cells

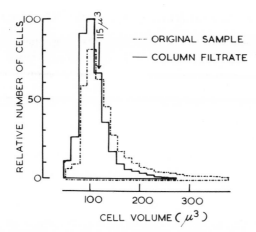

Fig. 6. Coulter Cell Counter volume distribution profiles of fowl blood lymphocytes. The lymphocytes (small, medium, and large) were initially purified by
separation of the buffy coat, followed by passage through an adherence-type cotton
wool column. This represents the original sample, which was passed through a size
filtration-type column of 50-70 μ diameter glass beads, to give, with 10% recovery,
a column filtrate fraction. The level of erythrocytes and other cell types in the
preparation was negligible (9).

smaller than 115 μ^3, the region of typical fowl blood small lymphocytes,
and a substantial depletion of cells larger than this, with complete
removal of cells greater than 270 μ^3.

A note of caution may be appropriate at this stage, before considering some applications of the filtration technique. To deplete the
preparations sufficiently of large cells, we are obliged to continue filtration until only 10% of the original opulation is recovered. This
poses the problem of whether this 10% really is representative of the
total population of small lymphocytes, or whether the column has
selected out a special cell type because of factors other than cell size.
As yet there is no suggestion of selection among undamaged cells by
any factor other than size, but it is difficult to eliminate experimentally
the participation of some completely unknown factor! Further objections to the method are its poor efficiency and low yield, and its inabil-
ity to produce a pure preparation of large as well as small cells. However, it serves as a temporary expedient until replaced by some
technique, perhaps a development of the Coulter Counter (1) which
will process around 10^9 cells in a reasonable time and allow complete
recovery of all cells in a series of defined size fractions.

III. SOME APPLICATIONS OF COLUMN SEPARATION

Two examples will be given to show the consequences of removing the relatively small number of large cells from lymphocyte preparations. The first example (Table II) is an application of the separation techniques to a biochemical problem. Mr. N. Kraft and I have been interested in the role of nucleases in the nucleic acid metabolism of lymphocytes (4). Thymic tissue, whose dominant cell type is a small lymphocyte, contains appreciable activities of two well-defined ribonucleases, termed on the basis of their pH optima acid and alkaline ribonuclease. A teased out preparation of rat thymic lymphocytes also shows both activities. However, after passage through a column to remove larger cells, the small lymphocytes, while still containing alkaline ribonuclease, are virtually free of acid ribonuclease activity. We must conclude that rat thymic tissue acid ribonuclease is concentrated in some minor cell component. This is likely to be a macrophage type of cell, since macrophages purified from rat peritoneal fluid by the Rabinowitz adherence technique (6) have enormous levels of ribonuclease activity. Results such as these emphasize the need to work at the cellular level, rather than to regard the tissue as a uniform mass.

The second example concerns cellular immunology and the nature of the cell initiating various immune reactions. The target cell is usu-

TABLE II

Ribonuclease Levels in Rat Cells [a]

	Units per mg protein $\times 10^8$	
	Total acid RNAase	Total alkaline RNAase
Whole thymus tissue	1.7	3.3
Purified thymic small lymphocytes	0.1	3.9
Purified peritoneal macrophages	67	60

[a] Ribonuclease activity was assayed at pH 5.8 (acid RNAase) or pH 7.8 (alkaline RNAase) by release of acid-alcohol-soluble ultraviolet absorbing nucleotides and oligonucleotides from repurified yeast RNA. Assays were performed after freezing and thawing to disrupt cells and granules, and in the case of alkaline RNAase, in the presence of p-chloromercuribenzoate to inactivate the ribonuclease inhibitor. One unit represents the equivalent of one microgram of crystalline pancreatic ribonuclease. The thymic small lymphocytes were isolated by the small glass bead size filtration technique, peritoneal macrophages by large glass bead active adherence columns (4).

TABLE III

Immunological Activity of Purified Small Lymphocytes

System	Lymphocyte source	Assay	Activity of pure small lymphocytes compared to activity of original cell suspension, %
Initiation of graft-versus-host reaction	Chick blood	Pocks on chorioallantoic membrane	122
	Mouse thoracic duct	Splenic enlargement	103
Initiation of immune response to antigen	Mouse thoracic duct	Sheep erythrocyte antigen; hemolytic foci in spleen	100
	Mouse thoracic duct	Salmonella flagellin antigen; serum titer	5

[a] All small lymphocyte preparations were obtained by the fine glass bead size filtration technique. In the case of chick blood, this was preceded by isolation of the buffy coat and separation of lymphocytes on active adherence cotton wool column. Details of assays are found in Szenberg and Shortman (8,9) and Nossal et al. (5).

ally considered to be a small lymphocyte, but activity has on occasion been ascribed to the large dividing cells present in the mixed populations available for experimental study. This problem is being investigated in a number of collaborative projects with Professor Nossal, Dr. Miller, and Dr. Szenberg in our laboratories. The method used is to compare the activity of lymphocytes on a per cell basis before and after removal of the larger cells on a glass bead column (Table III). In both the graft-versus-host systems we have investigated activity is undiminished or even slightly enhanced after passage through the column. The bulk of the capacity to initiate these responses may safely be ascribed to small lymphocytes. However, in the case of the immune response to an injected antigen the result varies with the type of antigen (or type of assay), even when the same cell preparation is employed for both assays. If the antigen is sheep erythrocytes the target cell or the majority of target cells can be considered to be small lymphocytes, as with the graft-versus-host activity. However, when bacterial flagellin is the antigen, most activity is lost on passage through the column. This suggests that the initiating cell is a larger cell or, if the interaction of several cells is required, that a limiting cell type was large in size.

Finally, a word of advice based on experience with both techniques. Neither procedure represents a formula for producing the appropriate result in an experiment based on blind faith. Neither procedure requires any special touch unique to the originator of the method. In both cases an attempt has been made to understand the basis by which the columns work, and to check the effect of the major variables. This information is meant to be used to obtain optimal separation with the cell preparation under study. This requires careful monitoring of cell recoveries and repeated checks on the purifications obtained. This may involve examination of the smeared and stained preparations and phase contrast microscopy, in addition to monitoring by other methods such as Coulter Counter size distribution profiles, tritiated thymidine uptake experiments or tests for phagocytic activity. Under these conditions useful and reproducible cell separations can be obtained.

References

1. M. J. Fulwyler, *Science*, **150,** 910 (1965).
2. J. E. Garvin, *J. Exptl. Med.*, **114,** 51 (1961).
3. S. Kovařík, *Folia Biol., Prague*, **9,** 388 (1963).
4. N. Kraft and K. Shortman, in preparation.

5. G. J. V. Nossal, K. Shortman, J. F. A. P. Miller, G. F. Mitchell, and J. S. Haskill, *Cold Spring Harbor Symp. Quant. Biol.*, **32,** 369 (1967).
6. Y. Rabinowitz, *Blood,* **23,** 811 (1964).
7. K. Shortman, *Australian J. Exptl. Biol. Med. Sci.,* **44,** 271 (1966).
8. A. Szenberg and K. Shortman, *Ann. N.Y. Acad. Sci.,* **129,** 310 (1966).
9. K. Shortman and A. Szenberg, *Australian J. Exptl. Biol. Med. Sci.,* in press.

Partition in Polymer Two-Phase Systems—Some Recent Results

PER-ÅKE ALBERTSSON

Department of Biochemistry, University of Umeå, Umeå, Sweden

I. INTRODUCTION

Progress in biochemistry and cell physiology depends to a great extent on developments of new techniques. Among these, methods for the fractionation of complex mixtures are of particular interest. By analyzing an extract of a tissue homogenate by physiochemical separation methods new components can be discovered and new relations between known components may be exposed. In this way the now classical methods of centrifugation, electrophoresis, and chromatography have been, and will be, of great importance for progress in biochemistry and related fields. Experience has taught us that it is often advantageous to combine different methods which complement each other in order to solve a fractionation problem. Particularly when dealing with large fragile complexes of macromolecules, such as cells and subcellular particles, the preparations under study are so heterogenous in size, form, density, charge, structure, and stability that effective purification can only be obtained by combining different methods.

For some years we have studied the possibility of using liquid–liquid partitioning for fractionation of particles and macromolecules. Extraction techniques have been used for a long time in chemistry. The solvents employed usually contain one or more organic solvents. Since these may destroy delicate macromolecular structures and extract lipids, it was necessary to develop special phase systems where both phases were aqueous in order to apply liquid–liquid distribution on macromolecules and cell particles. Such systems can be obtained by mixing water with two suitably different water-soluble polymers. In the phase systems thus obtained, particles, such as cells or cell organelles distribute according to their surface properties. Particles having different surface properties may therefore collect in different phases and a separation is obtained. Often particles will selectively collect at the interface of the phase system and this phenomenon is utilized for fractionation purposes. Soluble macromolecules like proteins or nucleic acids dissolve in the phase system—usually without significant adsorption at the interface—and their partition depends upon various macromolecular parameters such as molecular weight, charge, and conformation.

II. POLYMER PHASE SYSTEMS

Dextran and polyethylene glycol are two highly water-soluble polymers. However, when they are put together in the same solution, phase separation occurs, yielding two aqueous liquid phases, the lower one containing most of the dextran and the upper one most of the polyethylene glycol. Such incompatability is often observed in polymer mixtures and many, although not all, pairs of polymers give rise to liquid–liquid phase separation. For a detailed discussion on polymer phase systems and previous work in this field the reader is referred to reference 4.

Some pairs of polymers which have been used for constructing phase diagrams is shown in Table I. Both nonionic polymers such as dextran and polyethylene glycol or polyelectrolytes such as dextran sulfate may be used in various combinations. In the case of polyelectrolytes one obtains systems with liquid ion exchangers. Due to

TABLE I
Some Pairs of Polymers Which Have Been Used for Constructing Two-Phase Systems

Dextran–polyethylene glycol
Dextran–methylcellulose
Dextran–hydroxypropyldextran
Dextran sulfate–polyethylene glycol

the presence of the polymers the viscosity of the phases is high and, together with the small density difference, causes a long time of phase separation, the settling time being usually between 10 and 30 min. The settling time may be reduced considerably, however, by low speed centrifugation or by using thin layers of the phases (14).

We may compare the aqueous polymer phases with conventional solvents as is done in Figure 1. To the left in this figure a number of solvents is listed according to their hydrophobic–hydrophilic nature; at the bottom a salt solution, then water, acetone, etc., with increasing hydrophobicity, up to heptane. We may consider these as selected solvents from a continuous solvent spectrum with increasing hydrophobic character. If we want to place the polymer solutions in this spectrum it is obvious that, since they all contain mainly water, they should fall within in a very narrow part of the spectrum. To the right in Figure 1, a number of polymer solutions are listed according to the hydrophilic–hydrophobic nature of the polymers. The order between the polymers may be somewhat arbitrary but the main point is that we have a number of immiscible liquids which all are very close to each other on the solvent spectrum. This means that phase systems formed by these solvents can be expected to be selective in separating substances which themselves fall within the same aqueous part of the solvent spectrum, such as particles and macromolecules of biological origin.

By varying the properties of the polymers, one should, in theory, be able to vary the selectivity of the systems almost at will. For example, polymers with certain conformations and with certain groups—charged, hydrophilic or hydrophobic—should be very effective in selectively

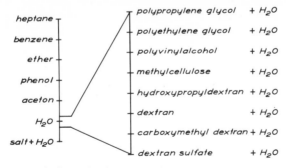

Fig. 1. Aqueous solutions of polymers to the right are all immiscible above certain concentrations of polymers. Being aqueous solutions with a high water content (90–99%) they all fall within the aqueous part of the solvent spectrum to the left.

extracting from a mixture those components to which the polymers have a specific affinity.

III. BEHAVIOR OF PARTICLES AND MACROMOLECULES IN POLYMER PHASE SYSTEMS

What factors determine the behavior of particles and macromolecules in polymer two-phase systems? A large number of partition experiments have given us some useful general ideas about the factors which determine partition behavior. The following generalizations may be made.

Size. The particle and molecular size has a great influence on the partition. Low molecular weight substances such as salts, sucrose, amino acids, etc., partition equally between the phases. Larger molecules concentrate more or less in one or the other phase. For very large molecules such as DNA or viruses the partition is unilateral, practically all the substances being found in one of the phases. Which phase a macromolecule prefers depends on other factors than size. For still larger particles such as mitochondria, chloroplasts, and whole cells, collection at the interface frequently occurs and this phenomena is utilized for the separation of these larger particles (see Section IV).

Conformation. Native and denatured DNA display very different partition behavior and this has been utilized for separation purposes (1,7,18,35,36). Denaturation of the proteins also causes a change in the partition coefficient. Upon denaturation of proteins and nucleic acids, previously hidden groups of the molecules are exposed to the surrounding phase and this may be one additional reason why denaturation causes a drastic change in partition.

Ionic Composition and Charge. In some phase systems the ionic composition has a very strong influence on the partition. It is mainly the ratio between the different ions which determines the partition coefficient but for many substances the overall salt concentration is also important. Figure 2 shows the partition coefficient for DNA in different salts. By changing the ratio between different salts a substance can be transferred almost completely from one phase to the other. This has been exploited for working out a method for isolating DNA (32). See also the chapter by Pettijohn in this volume.

The charge of the partitioned molecules or particles themselves is also of importance, as has been shown by Walter and collaborators (37). They found a correlation between electrophoretic mobility and partition of red blood cells; see the chapter by Walter in this volume.

The effect of salts on the partition shown in Figure 2 has been

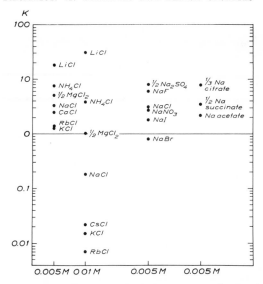

Fig. 2. Partition coefficient, K, of calf thymus DNA with different salts in a dextran–polyethylene glycol phase system. (For details see reference 8; see also Fig. 3 of chapter by Pettijohn, this volume.)

observed for many different kinds of substances including proteins, nucleic acids, viruses, bacteria, mitochondria, chloroplasts, and blood cells. In all these studies the partitioned particles carried a net negative charge.

There is, however, a distinct difference in the salt effect of positively charged particles compared to negatively charged particles. Thus negatively charged particles show a behavior like that in Figure 2. NaCl gives a lower K value than LiCl and NaSO$_4$ gives a higher K (partition coefficient) value than NaCl for example. But for positively charged particles the order between the effects of the different ions is reversed, so that NaCl gives higher K value than LiCl and Na$_2$SO$_4$. For positively charged particles the salt effect can thus be illustrated by turning the diagram in Figure 2 upside down. This has been demonstrated with various ion-exchange particles and polyelectrolytes (38). For proteins this charge effect can be illustrated by comparing the K values at different pH around the isoelectric point. Figure 3 shows the K value of egg albumin as a function of pH in NaCl and Na$_2$SO$_4$. The two curves intersect close to the isoelectric point. At this pH the salt effect is at a minimum.

The question arises what mechanism lies behind the salt effect on the distribution of particles and macromolecules. No definite answer

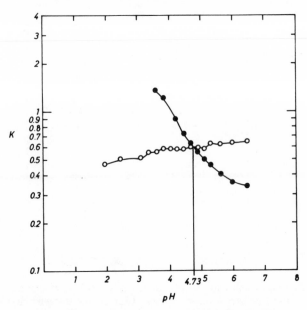

Fig. 3. Partition coefficient of egg albumin as a function of pH in two different salt media: $0.1M$ NaCl (filled circles); $0.05M$ Na$_2$SO$_4$ (open circles). Glycine and phosphate buffers were used at a concentration of $0.01M$.

can be given but one can imagine that ions change the properties of either the two phases or the partitioned substance or of both. Thus the ions could modify the water structure around the two-phase polymers, dextran and polyethylene glycol, for example, and thereby influence their interaction with the partitioned substance. Likewise, the ionic milieu of the phases would be expected to have a strong influence on the composition of the surface layers of the partitioned particles and thereby to influence the interaction between the particle and the phases. For example, in LiCl a charged particle would expose a completely different surface to its surroundings than, say, in NaCl. The same reasoning can be applied to proteins and nucleic acids.

Other Factors. The type of phase polymer and its molecular weight also influences the partition coefficient. In addition to size and charge other properties of the partitioned particles must determine their partition since particles with the same size and electrophoretic mobility can display rather different partition coefficients. We should expect that the number and location of hydrophobic and hydrophilic groups on the particle surface should influence partition. Our knowledge of particle or macromolecular surfaces is yet very limited, however, and a comparison between the properties of a particle surface (other except that size and net charge), can hardly be made. However, proteins of which the complete three-dimensional structure now is available should offer interesting and useful model substances to study the mechanism behind partition.

IV. FORCES BETWEEN PARTICLES AND PHASE

The characteristic behavior of macromolecules such as DNA, RNA, and proteins of high molecular weight is that the partitioned macromolecules easily can be transferred selectively from one phase to the other. Their behavior can be summarized qualitatively by the Brønsted formula (19)

$$c_1/c_2 = \exp(\lambda M/RT)$$

where c_1 and c_2 are the concentrations in the top and bottom phases, respectively, R is the gas constant, T the absolute temperature, M the molecular weight, and λ is a parameter which depends on other factors than M, such as the chemical composition and structure of the macromolecule and the properties of the phase system. For spherical particles M should be replaced by the particle's surface area. If M is very high, above 10^6, for example, λ can change very little and still give drastic charges in the K value (c_1/c_2). For example, if λ has a small positive value, the K value can still be very large provided M is large enough. If now λ is changed a little in some way, for example by slightly changing the phase composition, so that it has a small but negative value, the K value will drop and become very small. Likewise for two large molecules which differ very slightly in other respects than size, the λ values may differ only little but because M is large the K values of the two substances may be drastically different. Graphically we may illustrate this by Figure 4 where the K value is plotted against some change in phase composition for different hypothetical macromolecular substances. Qualitatively, the steepness of the curves is related to the size of the partitioned macromolecules whereas the position of the intercept with the x axis is related to λ, that is, to other factors than size.

What kind of forces act between the partitioned particles and the phases? We can imagine that hydrogen bonds and hydrophobic bonds are involved but their relative importance cannot be given at the moment. Ionic bonds in the case of polyelectrolyte systems may also be involved. However, I would like to stress that even very weak forces are enough to cause an almost unilateral distribution. The difference

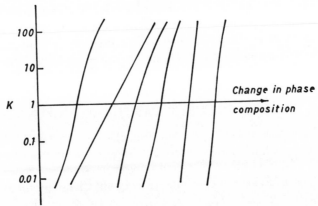

Fig. 4. Typical partition behavior of large molecules in polymer two-phase systems. A small change in phase composition causes a large change in K value. Low molecular weight substances usually have K values around 1 independent of phase composition.

in free energy between the two cases when the partitioned substance is in the upper phase and in the lower phase need only be about 3 kcal/mole to give a c_1/c_2 value of the order of 100. Thus a force of the order of one hydrogen bond *per molecule or particle* is enough to cause a fairly one-sided distribution. For a macromolecule this force can be a sum of many weak bonds spread out all over the exposed surface of the macromolecule. Each of these bonds is much weaker than a hydrogen bond but together they may add up to the same order of strength. For large molecules such as portein molecules or DNA molecules and also for particles this means that a number of extremely weak forces may be enough to cause a one-sided distribution. This also explains why delicate changes in phase composition can cause drastic changes in the distribution.

V. SOME APPLICATIONS

Polymer phase systems have had many applications for the fractionation both of macromolecules and particles.

Proteins. The general behavior of proteins is described in references 4–6. Okazaki and Kornberg applied a dextran–polyethylene glycol system for the purification of the enzyme DNA polymerase (27) (see also ref. 22). Capecchi used a similar system to separate proteins from nucleic acids (20). Babinet included partition in dextran–polyethylene glycol system in a procedure for the purification of RNA-polymerse (15). In all these methods one or a few partition steps were enough to achieve the desired fractionation. This allows fairly large-scale operations. The partition procedures were followed by other fractionation steps, which removed the polymers from the desired enzymes.

Countercurrent distribution with the dextran–polyethylene glycol system was applied on phosvitin by Mok et al. (24). Two major and one minor components were resolved after an experiment with 241 transfers.

Nucleic Acids. The general behavior of nucleic acids is described in reference 8 and applications on fractionation of nucleic acids are described in references 1–3,23,26a,28,32. For a general review on the partition of nucleic acids the reader is referred to the chapter by Pettijohn in this volume.

Viruses. Polymer two-phase systems have been applied both to large-scale purification of viruses in batch operations and for analytical purposes by countercurrent distribution of virus strains (9). Examples of virus concentration and purification are: phage T2 (9), phage ϕX174 (33,34), ECHO virus (29), polio virus (26), foot-and-mouth disease virus (21), and Japanese encephalitis virus (25). The main advantages with these procedures are that they are simple, can easily be scaled up, and give concentrated virus in a high yield. Applications on an industrial scale have also been reported (21).

Bengtsson and Philipson applied countercurrent distribution using a phase system of dextran sulfate–polyethylene glycol for analyzing various polio virus strains (16,17). Different strains displayed different distribution behavior and this could be related to genetic markers.

Cells. The general behavior of bacterial and algal cells and also of some red blood cells was studied by Albertsson and Baird (10). The application of countercurrent distribution on blood cells has been carried out by Walter and collaborators (37). A general review of this work is found in the chapter by Walter in this volume.

Chloroplasts and Mitochondria. The system dextran–polyethylene glycol has been used for countercurrent distribution of chloroplasts (11). Two components were resolved, one containing intact chloroplasts, probably with the surrounding chloroplast membrane intact and the other containing broken chloroplasts (see Fig. 5). Similar studies on rat liver mitochondria by Ericson in our laboratory have revealed a considerable heterogeneity in standard preparations of mitochondria.

Antigen–Antibody Complexes. If the partition coefficients of antigen, antibody, and antigen–antibody complexes are different, partition may be used for detection of antigen–antibody reactions (12) and also

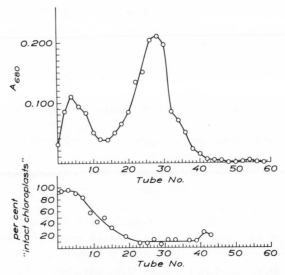

Fig. 5. Separation of chloroplasts into two classes; to the left, intact chloroplasts; to the right, broken chloroplasts (11).

to separate the different particle species present in an antigen–antibody mixture. These possibilities have been utilized by Philipson et al. to study the reaction between a virus and its antibodies (30,31). The redistribution of the virus as a result of antibody complex formation could be conveniently measured by using P^{32}-labeled polio virus. Countercurrent distribution was used to analyze the products obtained when polio virus was inactivated by antibody from human γG globulins. Uncombined virus could be separated from the virus–antibody complexes (Fig. 6).

VI. THIN LAYER COUNTERCURRENT DISTRIBUTION

Often the K values of different substances in a mixture are very close, and a sufficient separation is not achieved by single-step batch operations. Instead, multistage procedures at constant phase compositions have to be used. The well-known Craig countercurrent distribution technique is here very suitable. A drawback with the polymer phase systems is the long time needed for phase separation. This may be overcome, however, by employing thin layers of the phases. A special thin-layer countercurrent distribution apparatus has therefore been constructed (14) and used with success on many applications of polymer phase systems for fractionation of cell particles and macromolecules. A drawing of the unit is shown in Figure 7. Its main parts

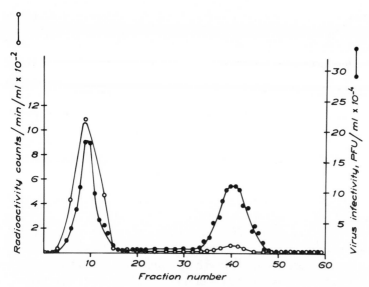

Fig. 6. Countercurrent distribution of P³²-labeled poliovirus mixed with antibody. To the right uncombined virus, to the left virus–antibody complex (31).

are two cylindrical plates, *d* and *e*, which rest upon each other. In each plate there are shallow cavities, *2* and *3*, which form the partition cells of lower and upper phase, respectively. The phases are mixed by rotary shaking and after settling the upper phases are transferred to adjacent partition cells by turning the upper plate relative to the lower plate. For details see reference 14. The important point of the apparatus is that the depth of the phase layer is only 1–2 mm. The

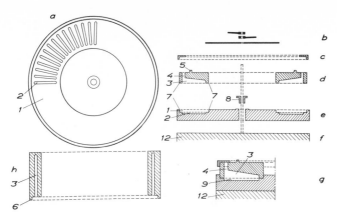

Fig. 7. Diagram of thin-layer countercurrent distribution apparatus (14).

settling time for polymer phase systems can thereby be decreased to 1–5 min from the 10–30 min needed with conventional types of counter-current distribution apparatus.

We have recently constructed a fully automatic version of the thin-layer distribution apparatus (see Fig. 8) and a commercial version of it is now available.* The apparatus has been applied for fractionation of chloroplasts (11), mitochondria (21a), red blood cells (37), viruses (31), and nucleic acids (26a).

VII. LIQUID–INTERFACE COUNTERCURRENT DISTRIBUTION

As I mentioned above, large particles such as chloroplasts, mitochondria, and whole cells often collect at the interface. This adsorption is reversible and the interface has a high capacity for adsorption because the interfacial area during shaking is very large. For separation purposes the distribution between one phase and the interface is therefore utilized for large particles in a similar fashion as the distribution between the two bulk phases utilized for soluble substances (see Fig. 9). The countercurrent distribution technique can also be used for systems

* Marketed by IRD, Box 11074, 161 11 Bromma 11, Sweden.

Fig. 8. Automatic version of the thin-layer countercurrent distribution apparatus.

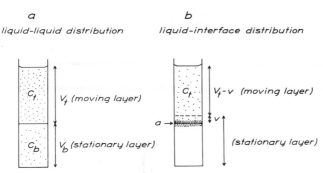

Fig. 9. When particles are distributed between the upper phase and the interface, liquid–interface distribution (right) is applied for separation. The interface material is included in the stationary layer. Compare with conventional countercurrent distribution (left) when the substance distributes between the bulk phases.

with liquid–interface distribution; ordinary countercurrent apparatus can then be applied. The only modification one has to introduce is to arrange the volume of the phases so that the interface is either kept stationary or carried over to the adjacent cell during each transfer. In this manner countercurrent distribution has been used for the fractionation of microorganisms (see Fig. 10) (10), blood cells (37) (see the chapter by Walter in this volume), chloroplasts (see Fig. 6) (11), and mitochondria (21a).

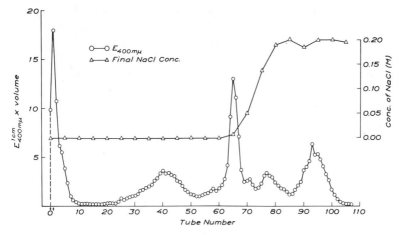

Fig. 10. Fractionation of microorganisms by liquid–interface countercurrent distribution. The peaks represent from left: yeast cells, *E. coli* K12, W1177, *E. coli* K12, 58, *Chlorella* (two small peaks), and *E. coli* ML3081.

VIII. REMOVAL OF POLYMERS

After a fractionation experiment is finished it is often desirable to remove the phase polymers from the substance of interest. In the case of large particles such as cells and cell fragments the polymers can be washed away by repeated centrifugations. Virus particles and DNA can also be recovered from the polymer by high speed centrifugation (1). In the case of proteins several different methods can be used, and for each protein a suitable recovery procedure can usually be devised. Precipitation or ion-exchange chromatography with DEAE-cellulose for example, have been used for a number of proteins. It would be desirable, however, to have a simple and general method which could be used routinely for recovering proteins from the phase polymers. Since proteins almost always are charged, electrophoresis should be the method of choice. Recent experiments in our laboratory have indicated that electrophoresis is suitable for recovery of proteins from dextran and polyethylene glycol.

IX. CONCLUDING REMARKS

The main characteristic of the polymer two-phase technique is that the procedure is mild and selective. In almost all experiments so far reported the biological activity under study has not been destroyed by the partitioning. The activities measured include enzyme activities, virus infectivity, photophosphorylation by chloroplasts, and oxidative phosphorylation by mitochondria. This mildness is probably partly due to the small interfacial tension between the phases. Also the presence of the polymers often stabilizes the distributed particles and macromolecules and protects them against denaturation. Of particular importance is that other factors than size, density, and charge can determine the distribution. The polymer two-phase system technique, therefore, is a useful complement to centrifugation and electrophoresis. For enzyme, nucleic acid, and virus purification, for example, the technique is best utilized in combination with other methods. If the two-phase technique is used in the earlier steps, other methods, for example centrifugation and chromatography, can remove the polymers at the same time as the desired substance is further purified.

Partition in polymer two-phase systems is, like all partition methods, a highly empirical method and systems suitable for practical separation purposes have to be set up after trial and error experiments. However, with the information now available on the partition behavior of different cells, cell organelles, viruses, nucleic acids, and proteins one can fairly well predict qualitatively the behavior of various particles and macromolecules. Thus, for example, the phase systems used for blood cells and bacteria can be used directly or with only slight modifications on other cells too. Once a suitable system has been found, the procedure for fractionation is simple and highly reliable.

References

1. B. Alberts, *Biochemistry,* **6,** 2527 (1967).
2. B. Alberts, in *Methods in Enzymology,* Vol. 12(A), S. P. Colowick and N. O. Kaplan, Eds., Academic Press, New York, 1967.
3. B. Alberts and P. Doty, *J. Mol. Biol.,* **32,** 379 (1968).
4. P. Å. Albertsson, *Partition of Cell Particles and Macromolecules,* Wiley, New York, Almquist and Wiksell, Stockholm, 1960.
5. P. Å. Albertsson and J. Nyns, *Nature,* **184,** 1465 (1959).
6. P. Å. Albertsson and J. Nyns, *Arkiv. Kemi,* **17,** 197 (1961).
7. P. Å. Albertsson, *Arch. Biochem. Biophys. Suppl.,* **1,** 264 (1962).
8. P. Å. Albertsson, *Biochim. Biophys. Acta,* **103,** 1 (1965).
9. P. Å. Albertsson, in *Methods of Virology,* Vol. 2, K. Maramorosch and H. Koprowski, Eds., 1967, Chapter 10, Academic Press, New York, 1967.
10. P. Å. Albertsson and G. D. Baird, *Exptl. Cell Res.,* **28,** 296 (1962).
11. P. Å. Albertsson and H. Baltscheffsky, *Biochem. Biophys. Res. Commun.,* **12,** 14 (1963).
12. P. Å. Albertsson and L. Philipson, *Nature,* **185,** 38 (1960).
13. P. Å. Albertsson and G. Blomqvist, to be published.
14. P. Å. Albertsson, *Anal. Biochem.,* **11,** 121 (1965).
15. C. Babinet, *Biochem. Biophys. Res. Commun.,* **26,** 639 (1967).
16. S. Bengtsson, L. Philipson, and P. Å. Albertsson, *Biochem. Biophys. Res. Commun.,* **9,** 318 (1962).
17. S. Bengtsson and L. Philipson, *Virology,* **20,** 176 (1963).
18. F. J. Bollum, *Cold Spring Harbor Symp. Quant. Biol.,* **28,** 21 (1963).
19. J. N. Brønsted, *Z. Physik. Chem. Ser. A (Bodenstein-Festband),* **1931,** 257.
20. M. R. Capecchi, *Proc. Natl. Acad. Sci. U.S.,* **58,** 1144 (1967).
21. Belg. Pat. (Derwent) No. 11716 (1962).
21a. I. Ericson, unpublished.
22. A. Falaschi and A. Kornberg, *J. Biol. Chem.,* **241,** 1478 (1966).
23. J. Favre and D. E. Pettijohn, *European J. Biochem,* **3,** 33 (1967).
24. C. C. Mok, C. T. Grant, and G. Taborsky, *Biochemistry,* **5,** 2517 (1966).
25. H. Nakai, *Acta Virol.,* **9,** 89 (1965).
26. E. C. J. Norrby and P. Å. Albertsson, *Nature,* **188,** 1047 (1960).
26a. B. Öberg, P. Å. Albertsson, and L. Philipson, *Biochim. Biophys. Acta,* **108,** 173 (1965).
27. T. Okazaki and A. Kornberg, *J. Biol. Chem.,* **239,** 259 (1964).
28. D. E. Pettijohn, *European J. Biochem,* **3,** 25 (1967).
29. L. Philipson, P. Å. Albertsson, and G. Frick, *Virology,* **11,** 553 (1960).
30. L. Philipson, J. Killander, and P. Å. Albertsson, *Virology,* **28,** 22 (1966).
31. L. Philipson, *Virology,* **28,** 35 (1966).
32. L. Rudin and P. Å. Albertsson, *Biochim. Biophys. Acta,* **134,** 37 (1967).

33. J. Sedat and R. L. Sinsheimer, *J. Mol. Biol.*, **9,** 489 (1964).
34. R. L. Sinsheimer, in *Procedures of Nucleic Acids Research*, G. L. Cantoni and D. R. Davies, Eds., Harper & Row, New York, 1966, p. 569.
35. W. C. Summers and W. Szybalski, *J. Mol. Biol.*, **26,** 107 (1967).
36. W. C. Summers and W. Szybalski, *J. Mol. Biol.*, **26,** 227 (1967).
37. H. Walter, *Protides Biol. Fluids, Proc. Colloq.*, **15,** 367 (1967).
38. H. Walter, R. Garza, and R. P. Coyle, *Biochim. Biophys. Acta.*, **156,** 409 (1968).
39. M. Watanabe and J. T. August, in *Methods of Virology*, Vol. 3, K. Maramorosch and H. Koprowski, Eds., Academic Press, New York, 1967, p. 99.

Factors in the Partition of Blood Cells in Aqueous Dextran–Polyethylene Glycol Two-Phase Systems

HARRY WALTER

Laboratory of Chemical Biology, Veterans Administration Hospital, Long Beach, and the Department of Biological Chemistry, UCLA School of Medicine, Los Angeles, California

Our interest in possible alterations of erythrocytic proteins as a function of red blood cell age prompted us to search for a good method for the separation of these cells on the basis of age. Our success in this endeavor with countercurrent distribution of red blood cells in polymer two-phase systems encouraged us to extend our study to factors involved in the partition of cells and, conversely, in using partition of cells as one indicator of some of their surface characteristics. Partition, as will be shown, has proved to be useful in demonstrating alterations in surface properties of red cells as a function not only of their age (1,2) but also of storage *in vitro* (3), chemical constituents of their membrane (4,5), and chemical or enzymological modification of their membranes (6). The usefulness of countercurrent distribution is further illustrated by our ability to separate reticulocytes (from phenylhydrazine-injected rats) into at least two populations (7); to separate red blood cells from white blood cells and white blood cells from each other (8); and to demonstrate similarities in surface properties between red blood cells and platelets from the same species. Experiments with reticulocyte ribosomes have also revealed a different partition for polysomes and monosomes.

It should be mentioned at the outset that all tested, negatively charged cells and particles behave in a manner analogous to that described for red cells with regard to the variables affecting their partition.

The advantages of working with red blood cells (RBC) are many. The cells can be easily obtained. They have a known lifespan. Their specific gravity, surface charge, and size change as a function of their age, giving a number of handles by which they can be separated.

Finally, there is no protein synthesis in mature red cells. The age of the proteins (hemoglobin, enzymes, membrane) in the separated cells is thus the same as that of the cells.

When aqueous solutions of different polymers are mixed, they often form immiscible phase systems. Albertsson (9,10) has used such systems to partition cells, particles, and macromolecules. He also studied the behavior of these materials and of such phase systems in a systematic manner. The great advantages of polymer two-phase systems include that they can be buffered, made isotonic (if necessary), have a great protective effect on the partitioned cells, and, in general, are mild enough to permit countercurrent distribution (CCD) of cells or particles without apparent damage.

In Figure 1 a phase diagram is presented using the polymers dextran [dextran (D) 500, Pharmacia, Uppsala, Sweden] and polyethylene glycol (PEG 6000, Union Carbide, Los Angeles). The work to be discussed was done using D–PEG phases; and usually 5% D (w/w)– 4% PEG (w/w) systems. These were found to give reasonable partitions for most of the cells we studied and also to settle in a reasonable time. One of the factors that affects the partition of cells is the proximity of the selected phase system to the critical point. The further the system is from the critical point the lower the partition coefficient. Conversely, the closer to the critical point, the higher the partition coefficient. However, close to the critical point the reproducibility of partition is poor, the settling time is increased, and other factors which affect partition of cells (e.g., salt composition of the phase system), no longer play a major role. This is demonstrated in

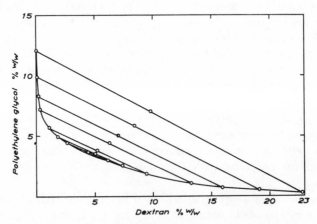

Fig. 1. Phase diagram of the dextran 500-polyethylene glycol 6000 system at 20° C. (From ref. 9, page 41.)

Figure 2, which shows (Fig. 2a) the partition of RBC from a number of different species (●, dog; ○, human; ×, sheep; △, rabbit) expressed as quantity of cells in the top phase (percent of total added) in a 5% D–4% PEG phase system. A number of points should be noted: (1) an increase in NaCl concentration with a concomitant decrease in phosphate buffer concentration (to keep the overall salt concentration isotonic) results in a decrease in the partition coefficient for the red cells of all the species tested; (2) the partition of erythrocytes appears to be species dependent; and (3) the drop in the partition coefficient with increasing NaCl concentration for the various species is sequential (i.e., dog RBC always have a greater partition than human RBC, etc.). In Figure 2b, the partition behavior of dog and rabbit RBC is shown in a phase system containing 5% D–3.5% PEG. This system is closer to the critical point, and it can be seen that (1) the partition of cells is increased and (2) that they are no longer affected by the NaCl–phosphate buffer ratio. In addition to these findings by Albertsson (10), he has studied the effect on the partition of cells and particles of various cations and anions and has shown that many of these fall into series causing an increasing (or decreasing) partition for all negatively charged cells or particles tested (9).

The work described so far is by Albertsson and co-workers (9,10) and led to our interest and subsequent involvement in partition and CCD studies on blood cells.

Since, as mentioned earlier, red cells age and during the aging process increase their specific gravity and diminish their surface charge and size, we thought it possible that one or more of these alterations might enable us to segregate erythrocytes on the basis of their age by CCD (1,2,5). Rats were injected with radioactive iron (^{59}Fe-ferrous

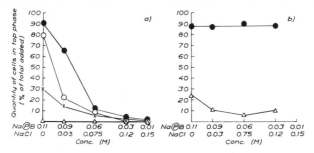

Fig. 2. The quantity of mammalian erythrocytes of different species found in the top phase of a system containing 5% (w/w) dextran–4% (w/w) PEG (a); and 5% (w/w) dextran–3.5% (w/w) PEG (b); at different sodium chloride and sodium phosphate buffer (pH 6.8) concentrations. (●) dog; (○) human; (×) sheep; (△) rabbit. (From ref. 10, Fig. 7).

citrate) and bled at different times after injection. This gave rise to
normal erythrocyte populations in which RBC of different, specific
ages (equal to the time elapsed between isotope injection and bleeding)
were labeled. Such RBC populations were subjected to CCD (47
transfers) in a phase system containing 5% D–4% PEG, 0.12M NaCl
and 0.03M phosphate buffer (pH 6.8). The cells were collected, lysed,
and analyzed for hemoglobin absorbance and relative specific radioactivity (rsa), defined as:

$$\frac{\text{counts/min/hemoglobin absorbance in a given sample}}{\text{counts/min/hemoglobin absorbance in a hemolyzed aliquot of the original cell population}}$$

The results of these experiments are presented in Figure 3. In Figures

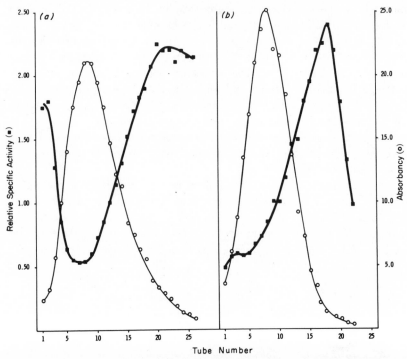

Fig. 3. Results of countercurrent distribution of rat red blood cells labeled with
[59Fe] ferrous citrate. Rats were exsanguinated at different times after injection
giving rise to labeled red blood cell populations of distinct ages. Relative specific
activities above 1.00 indicate higher concentrations of red cells of ages corresponding to the time elapsed between injection and bleeding. ○, red blood cell concentration (in terms of hemoglobin absorbance); ■, relative specific activity. For
details see text. Red blood cells were collected at the following times subsequent
to injection of isotope: *a*, 2 days; *b*, 10 days; *c*, 20 days; *d*, 30 days; *e*, 41 days;
f, 48 days; *g*, 54 days; and *h*, 65 days. Parts *c* and *d* are on page 125, *e* and *f* on
page 126, and *g* and *h* on page 127. (From ref. 2. See also ref. 5.)

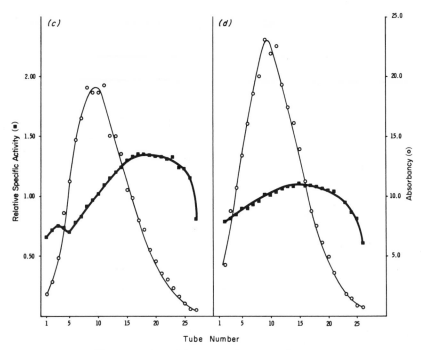

Fig. 3 (*continued*). See page 124 for explanation.

3*a–h* the curve depicting the CCD (open circles) of the rat RBC is the same since it represents the normal red cell population and is, obviously, not affected by the radioisotopic label. In Figure 3*a* one can see the rsa obtained with a cell population 2 days after injection of ^{59}Fe. In this graph rsa values above 1.00 indicate cells 2 days old and younger. It is readily apparent that there are two populations of young cells: one associated with the left end of the distribution curve and the second associated with the right end of the curve. In Figure 3*b*, run with blood obtained 10 days after injection, the left-hand peak has considerably diminished, while the right peak has shifted (slightly) toward the left. Figures 3*c* (20 days after injection) and 3*d* (30 days after injection) show a continuation of this trend. In Figure 3*e* (41 days after injection) the peak of the rsa curve has shifted from the right half to the left half of the distribution curve; Figure 3*f* represents data obtained 48 days after injection. Since the lifespan of the red blood cell in the rat is approximately 55 days, these last graphs represent the distribution of "old" red cells. Sometimes, instead of the rsa curve depicted in Figure 3*f,* we obtain a curve which still shows a distinct peak in the left region, sometimes not.

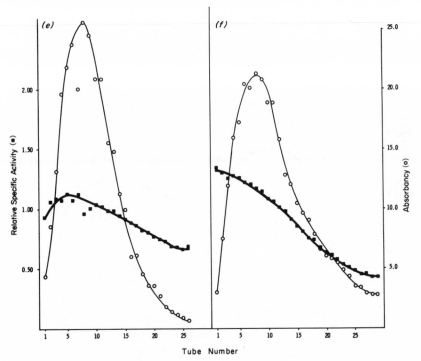

Fig. 3 (*continued*). See page 124 for explanation.

These variations in rats probably result from slight differences in the red cell lifespan.

In Figure 3*g* (54 days after injection) we have the first indication of rsa "peaks" reappearing at the ends of the distribution curve. This is due to the breakdown of erythrocytes (55-day lifespan as mentioned above) and the subsequent reutilization of the radioactive iron in the formation of new or young red cells. This process is more clearly evident in Figure 3*h* (65 days after injection) which has a striking resemblance to Figure 3*a* and in which, once again, the young cells carry the label.

The presence of two populations of young red cells (Figure 3*a*) attracted our attention, and we set out to determine whether one of these may represent reticulocytes and the other mature young erythrocytes (2). Rats were repeatedly injected with phenylhydrazine which causes them to develop a reticulocytosis. Red cells containing about 50% reticulocytes were subjected to CCD (Fig. 4), and the curve obtained (crosses) shows a distinct displacement to the left when compared to the distribution of a normal rat red cell population

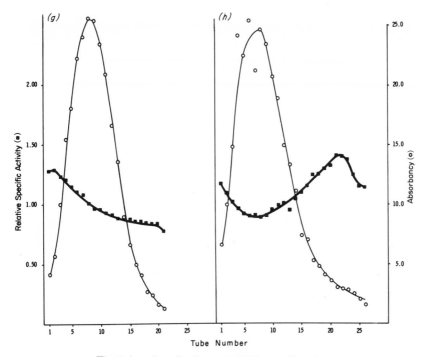

Fig. 3 (*continued*). See page 124 for explanation.

(open circles). This led us to the preliminary conclusion (see below) that the young red cell population associated with the left end of the normal distribution curve (Fig. 3a) represents reticulocytes, and the right end of the distribution curve must comprise mature young erythrocytes (since these are the only other young red cells present). A composite curve summarizing our data so far is presented in Figure 5. Reticulocytes as just mentioned are shown on the left end of the distribution of a normal cell population; as these mature to form young erythrocytes, an unexplained "jump" occurs from one end of the distribution curve (left) to the other (right). The 2-day-old erythrocytes are on the right side of the curve. By plotting the peaks of the rsa curves associated with the elapsed time between injection and bleeding one sees the systematic, progressive aging of the red blood cell through the rest of the distribution curve. Red blood cells of slightly different ages are thus shown to have distinct distribution patterns.

Our conclusion concerning the partition of reticulocytes proved to be only partially correct. The development by Albertsson of a "thin-layer countercurrent distribution apparatus" in which the phase

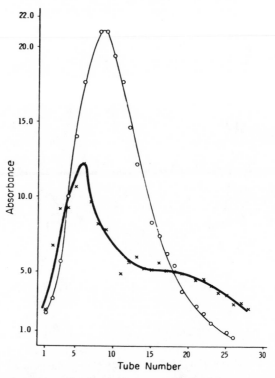

Fig. 4. Countercurrent distribution of red blood cells from a rat repeatedly injected with phenylhydrazine and having about 50% reticulocytes (×). Other curve (○) shows distribution pattern of a normal rat red blood cell population. (From ref. 2.)

settling time is drastically reduced, permitted an increase in the number of transfers that could now be made with cells (11). When red cell populations containing more than 90% reticulocytes (from phenylhydrazine-treated rats) were subjected to CCD (120 transfers, in a phase system containing 5% D–4% PEG, 0.09M Na-phosphate buffer, pH 6.8, and 0.03M NaCl), it became apparent that at least two populations of reticulocytes (Fig. 6, solid circles) were resolved (7).* One of these is associated with the left end of the normal distribution (Fig. 6, open circles) and the other with the right end. It thus appears that one of the reticulocyte populations (right end) has surface characteristics which are similar to those of mature young erythrocytes which are also found in this part of the normal distri-

* Experiment conducted while the author spent a sabbatical in the laboratory of Prof. Per-Åke Albertsson (spring 1966), Umeå, Sweden.

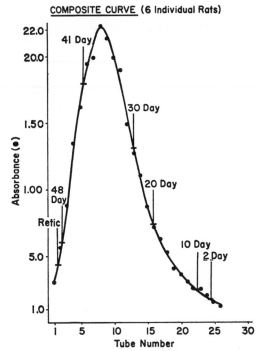

Fig. 5. Composite curve of the countercurrent distribution of radioactively labeled red blood cells obtained from six individual rats at different times after injection. The graph indicates the approximate location of the red blood cells of indicated ages in the normal distribution curve. See text for details. (From ref. 2).

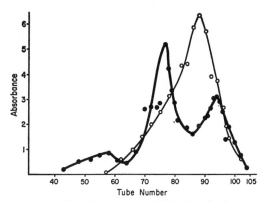

Fig. 6. Countercurrent distribution of red blood cells from a rat repeatedly injected with phenylhydrazine and having 97% reticulocytes (●). Other curve (○) shows distribution pattern of a normal rat red cell population. Red blood cell concentration is given in terms of hemoglobin absorbance. (From ref. 7.)

bution (see Fig. 5). It is possible that we have resolved reticulocytes of different ages (degrees of maturity), with the younger reticulocytes to the left, the older to the right. The cause for a "jump" from the left to the right side of the normal distribution curve during maturation is still not clear. It has been reported, however, that young reticulocytes show considerable invaginations (on examination by electron microscopy) as well as amoeboid-like movements (12,13). Such differences in surface characteristics between young and old reticulocytes might well be responsible for the different partitions observed.

In Figure 7 we show that the separability of red blood cells of different ages by countercurrent distribution appears to be a general phenomenon. The labeled red cells of dog (Fig. 7B), mouse (Fig. 7C) and even the nucleated red cells of the chicken (Fig. 7A), all obtained after 5–10% of their respective red cell lifespans had elapsed between isotope injection and bleeding, give data comparable to those described for the rat.

We now were most interested in determining what factor(s) permitted the separability on the basis of erythrocyte age. As indicated above, the specific gravity of red cells increases during their life while their size diminishes. These properties were thus the first to which we turned our attention. Since reticulocytes and mature young erythrocytes have the lowest specific gravity and the largest size, and these cells (young reticulocytes and old reticulocytes+mature young erythrocytes) are found on opposite sides of the distribution curve of a normal red cell population (Fig. 3A), it seemed unlikely that specific gravity and size were primary determinants in the partition of these cells. Electrophoretic mobility of reticulocytes has been reported to be lower than that of erythrocytes (14). Young erythrocytes, however, have a greater mobility than older erythrocytes (15).

We therefore turned our attention to surface charge. Sialic acid has been reported to account for about 65% of the surface charge of RBC (16). An analysis of the quantity of sialic acid associated with membranes of human (or rat) RBC in the different tubes of the extraction train following CCD showed (Fig. 8) that it (i.e., sialic acid/Hb OD) is constant. Therefore, an alteration in surface charge is likely to be an *effective* change that is not reflected in the actual amount of sialic acid found. In further pursuing this problem we sought data from the literature with which the partition of red cells could, perhaps, be correlated. A good correlation was indeed found (5) when the partition of erythrocytes from 10 different species (in a system containing 5% D–4% PEG, 0.09M Na phosphate, and 0.03M

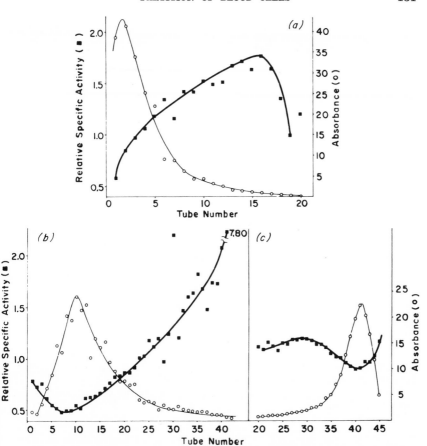

Fig. 7. Countercurrent distributions of red blood cells from (a) chicken, (b) dog, and (c) mice labeled with ^{59}Fe. Blood was collected from the animals within a few days after injection, making the young red blood cells those that carry the label. Relative specific activities above 1.00 indicate cells younger than average. ■, relative specific activity; ○, red blood cell concentration (in terms of hemoglobin absorbance). (From ref. 4. See also ref. 5.)

NaCl) was plotted against their relative electrophoretic mobilities (Fig. 9). Horse, rat, and mouse form exceptions while the surface charge of rabbit is, apparently, below the minimum required to obtain any partition for these cells. The apparent exceptions of horse and rat can at least be partially explained. An excellent correlation has been found between sialic acid molecules/unit surface area of red cells and red cell electrophoretic mobility for a number of species. Horse red cells are again an exception (17). Rat red cells appear to

132　　　　　　　　　　　H. WALTER

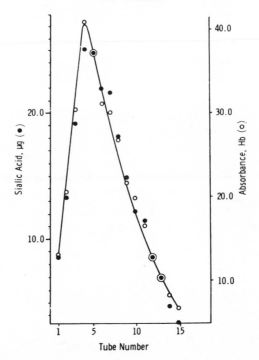

Fig. 8. Stromal sialic acid content from human red blood cells of different ages. Human red blood cells were distributed on the countercurrent apparatus. ○, red cell concentration in terms of hemoglobin absorbance and ●, μg sialic acid. (From ref. 4. See also ref. 5.)

have their sialic acid molecules bound to the red cell in an unusual manner, different from that of the other species' cells (18). Our conclusion, on the basis of the foregoing, is that mouse red cell membranes would similarly be found to display some chemical and/or physical difference when compared to that of the other species.

Surface charge, then, appears to be a determinant in the partition of red cells. The cells with highest charge have the greatest partition coefficient. Young erythrocytes, which have a higher surface charge than older cells, similarly display an increased partition (see Fig. 3a). The role of surface charge in determining the partition of cells is also borne out by the finding that neuraminidase-treated red blood cells not only have reduced electrophoretic mobilities but also diminished partition coefficients (6).

So far I have outlined the effects of polymer composition, salt composition and cell charge on the partition of cells and how red cells of different ages, or reticulocytes (from phenylhydrazine-treated rats

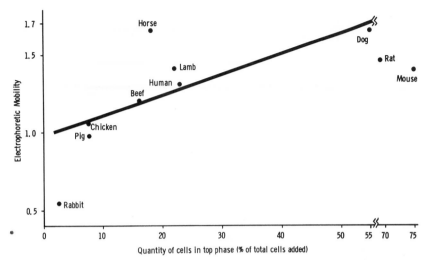

Fig. 9. Relationship between the electrophoretic mobilities of red blood cells from 10 different species and the quantities of these cells found in the top phase of a system containing dextran, 5% (w/w) ; polyethylene glycol, 4% (w/w) ; 0.09M phosphate buffer (pH 6.8) ; 0.03M NaCl. (From ref. 5.)

and of apparently different degrees of maturation), can be resolved by CCD. Now I wish to turn to a number of related problems so that a few of the large number of possible modifications of these phase systems can be seen. Such modifications can then be applied to the solution of specific problems.

Rabbit red blood cells have a low surface charge and can not be readily partitioned in the nonionic (dextran–polyethylene glycol) phase systems (Fig. 9). Since most of the current work described in the literature on reticulocytes is with rabbit cells, it seemed of interest to determine whether a suitable system for the partition of these cells (at the same time of cells of low surface charge in general) could be developed. The addition of small quantities of the cationic polymer DEAE–dextran (DEAE–D) to some of the dextran–polyethylene glycol phase systems led to interesting results. When 0.1% (w/w) DEAE–dextran (containing 3.17% N) was incorporated in a phase system which contained 5% D–4% PEG, the indicated partitions for rabbit (upper part, open squares of Fig. 10) and dog (lower part, open circles of Fig. 10) were obtained (19). For the sake of comparison (same figure, filled circles and squares) the partition of these cells is shown in a phase system without the DEAE–D. A striking and obvious difference between the partition of RBC in phases with and

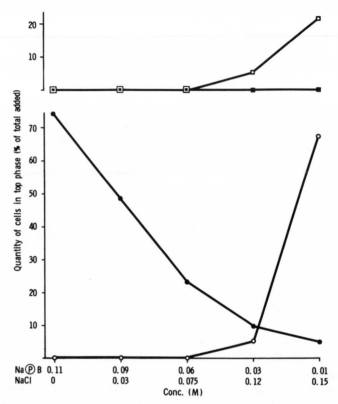

Fig. 10. Partition studies on rabbit (squares) and dog (circles) red blood cells. Solid squares and circles are partitions in a phase system containing dextran (5%, w/w), polyethylene glycol (4%, w/w) and the indicated salt compositions. Open squares and circles are partitions in a phase system containing dextran (5%, w/w), polyethylene glycol (4%, w/w), DEAE-dextran (0.1%, w/w) and the indicated salt compositions. The buffer is composed of equimolar parts of Na_2HPO_4 and NaH_2PO_4. (From ref. 19.)

without DEAE–D is that the NaCl–phosphate ratio (see discussion in relation to Fig. 2) has opposite effects. In the presence of DEAE–D, an increase in the NaCl–phosphate ratio causes an increase in the partition coefficient of RBC. In Figure 11 the partition of dog (circles) and rabbit RBC (squares) are presented in a phase system containing 5% D–4% PEG, 0.15M NaCl, and 0.01M Na-phosphate buffer (pH 6.8) and the indicated amounts of DEAE–D. Increasing the amounts of DEAE–D up to 0.1% obviously leads to increased partitions for these cells. By increasing the DEAE–D above 0.1% in this system, we get substantially farther from the critical point, and the partitions

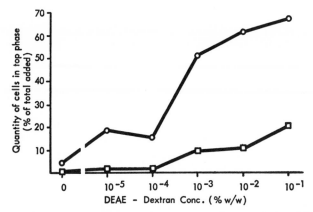

Fig. 11. Partition studies on rabbit (squares) and dog (circles) red blood cells. Partitions were carried out in a phase system containing dextran (5%, w/w), polyethylene glycol (4%, w/w), 0.15 M NaCl, 0.01M Na$_2$PHO$_4$–NaH$_2$PO$_4$ buffer and the indicated amounts of DEAE–dextran. (From ref. 19.)

are no longer increased and, eventually, are even decreased. In a phase system containing 4% D–4% PEG and 1% DEAE–D and 0.15M NaCl, 0.01M Na-phosphate buffer, we have a phase system which is no further from the critical point than the 5% D–4% PEG system, settles at a similar rate but gives approximately 60% of the rabbit cells in the top phase. Rabbit red cells can now be subjected to CCD and their young and old RBC separated by this method.

Albertsson has shown that the substitution of K$^+$ salts by Na$^+$ salts by Li$^+$salts in a given phase system leads to an increase in the partition of cells, particles, and macromolecules tested (9). As demonstrated in Table I, (dog) red cells behave in line with Albertsson's findings.

TABLE I [a]

Effect of Cations on the Partition [b] of Dog Red Blood Cells in Dextran–
Polyethylene Glycol Systems with and without DEAE-Dextran

System	Cation used		
	K	Na	Li
Dextran (5%, w/w), polyethylene glycol (4%, w/w), 0.09M phosphate, 0.03M chloride	24	45	86
Dextran (5%, w/w), polyethylene glycol (4%, w/w), DEAE–dextran (0.1%, w/w), 0.01M phosphate, 0.15M chloride	65	69	25

[a] From H. Walter and F. W. Selby, *Biochim. Biophys. Acta*, **148**, 517 (1967).
[b] Expressed as quantity of cells in top phase (% of total cells added).

136   H. WALTER

However, the incorporation of 0.1% DEAE–D leads to a reversal of this series. Thus the partition of red cells in a phase system containing K^+ and Na^+ salts gives similar partitions while in the presence of Li^+ salts a striking decrease in the partition takes place. This led us to suspect that the DEAE–D may, as a positively charged material, behave in a manner opposite (with respect to salt dependence) to that of the negatively charged particles, cells, and macromolecules previously investigated. Phase systems composed of 4% D–4% PEG–1.04% DEAE–D and containing (a) no salt, or (b) 0.15M NaCl + 0.01M Na-phosphate buffer (pH 6.8), or (c) 0.11M Na-phosphate buffer were prepared. The systems were mixed, permitted to settle and the top and bottom phases separated to determine the partition of the DEAE–D (20). Micro-Kjeldahl determinations for nitrogen were performed (since the DEAE–D was the only nitrogen-containing material present). The results of these experiments are presented in Table II. In the absence of salt, DEAE–D partitions almost evenly between the top and bottom phases. NaCl pushes almost all of the DEAE–D into the top phase while phosphate forces the DEAE–D into the bottom phase. These changes in the partition are reflected to some extent in the relative phase volumes observed in the presence of NaCl, phosphate or in the absence of any salt.

It appears that the positively charged DEAE–D does indeed partition in a manner opposite to that of negatively charged cells, particles, and macromolecules with regard to salt dependence. The partition of cells in phase systems containing the cationic polymer can now be

TABLE II [a]

Partition of DEAE–Dextran in a Dextran–Polyethylene Glycol Two-Phase System

Phase [b]	Salt composition	DEAE-D Partition (mg N/g phase)	Rel. phase vol.
Top	NaCl (0.15M) +	0.472	0.68
Bottom	Na-phosphate buffer (0.01M) [c]	0.025	0.32
Top	None present	0.339	0.58
Bottom		0.325	0.42
Top	Na-phosphate buffer (0.11M)	0.023	0.52
Bottom		0.635	0.48

[a] From H. Walter, R. Garza, and R. P. Coyle, *Biochim. Biophys. Acta,* **156,** 409 (1968).

[b] Total phase composition: dextran (4%, w/w), polyethylene glycol (4%, w/w), DEAE-dextran (1.04%, w/w), plus salts indicated.

[c] Na-phosphate buffer is composed of equimolar parts of Na_2HPO_4 and NaH_2PO_4.

better understood. The primary effect of the salt appears to be on the DEAE–D. The positively charged polymer, by interacting with the negatively charged cells, makes the latter partition in a manner which is opposite (with regard to salt dependence) to that found in the absence of the cationic polymer. While systems containing DEAE–D are useful for the partition of cells of low surface charge, it must be pointed out that the interaction between DEAE–D and the cell membrane is difficult, if not impossible, to reverse.

Because of our interest in studying enzyme and membrane proteins from RBC of different ages, it is important to work with erythrocytes that are not contaminated with leukocytes. We therefore turned our attention to the partition of leukocytes from a number of species under discussion and found that the partitions are such that separations of erythrocytes and leukocytes are feasible for a number of species (and particularly for rabbit and rat). Details of these experiments will be published elsewhere (8). It is of interest, however, to mention here that the partition coefficient of human leukocytes is greater than that of human erythrocytes. This finding is opposite to that reported for the relative electrophoretic mobilities of these cells and leads to the question of what factors in addition to surface charge might be involved in the partition of cells.

Our experiments with white cells naturally also lead to the question of whether granulocytes and lymphocytes could be resolved by CCD. We have only begun these investigations but, in Figure 12, we show

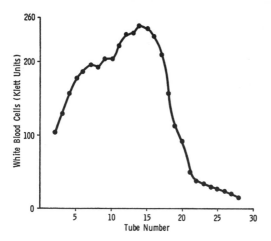

Fig. 12. Countercurrent distribution of lamb leukocytes in a phase system containing dextran, 5% (w/w); polyethylene glycol, 4% (w/w); and 0.11M Na-phosphate buffer (pH 6.8). 30 transfers were completed.

the distribution curve of clean white blood cells from lamb. They were subjected to 30 transfers on a thin-layer CCD apparatus in a phase system composed of 5% D–4% PEG and $0.11M$ Na-phosphate buffer, pH 6.8. The obvious heterogeneity of the leukocyte population is clearly revealed by the distribution curve and leads us to hope that a resolution will indeed be possible with a larger number of transfers.

We have also partitioned platelets (Fig. 13) obtained from a number of different species (in 5% D–4% PEG and $0.11M$ Na-phosphate buffer) and have, to our surprise, found that the partitions of platelets and erythrocytes from the same species are remarkably similar [with the exceptions of rabbit, horse, and of rat (in another phase system)]. This indicates that erythrocytes and platelets in a given species have surface properties that are similar, at least insofar as those characteris-

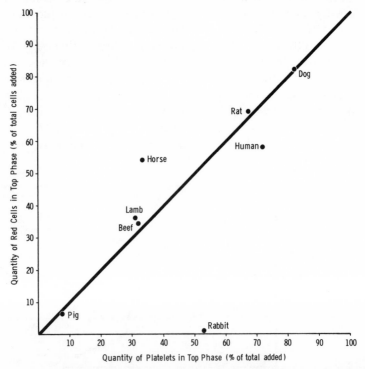

Fig. 13. Relationship between the partition of red blood cells and the partition of platelets from different species. Phase system contained dextran, 5% (w/w); polyethylene glycol, 4% (w/w); and $0.11M$ Na-phosphate buffer (pH 6.8). Partitions are expressed as quantity of cells in top phase (% of total added). (From ref. 21.) (The figure is corrected according to later results.)

tics which determine partition are concerned. Countercurrent curves of platelets show single, essentially normal distributions.

Alterations of red cell behavior as a function of *in vitro* storage are readily apparent in partition studies. Red blood cells stored in ACD for periods longer than 3 weeks have been reported to be rapidly cleared from the blood of recipients. The partition of red cells increases (Table III) on storage after a period of about 3 weeks. It has also been shown that the addition of adenosine (or adenine) to ACD during the storage period leads to considerably improved (lengthened) survival times in the blood of recipients. We have found that the addition of adenosine (or adenine) to ACD during red cell storage prevents alterations in the partition. While we can make no direct correlative statements between the survival time of red cells that have been stored *in vitro* and their partition behavior, the results are certainly suggestive. If the analogy between surface charge and partition of red cells holds, one may conclude that the effective surface charge of erythrocytes is increased during storage in ACD. This change appears to be opposite to the one which takes place during *in vivo* aging of erythrocytes (see Fig. 5). It must, however, be noted that Ruhenstroth-Bauer has reported no difference in electrophoretic mobility between fresh and stored erythrocytes. If this is so, it may very well point to factors involved in partition of cells in addition to surface charge, such as (for example) the metabolic state of the partitioned cell.

Finally, I wish to mention a few other factors that have distinct effects on the partition of cells and can therefore be used to change the partition of cells or particles of particular interest to one that may be particularly useful in a given study. In those dextran–polyethylene

TABLE III [a]

Partition of Fresh and Stored Human Erythrocytes [b]

	Partition [c]
Fresh erythrocytes	57
Stored erythrocytes	
28–29 days	74
42–43 days	83

[a] Phase system contained 5% (w/w) dextran, 4% (w/w) polyethylene glycol and 0.11M Na-phosphate buffer (pH 6.8).

[b] Taken from H. Walter, in H. Peeters, Ed., *Protides Biol. Fluids, Proc. Colloq.*, **15**, 367 (1968).

[c] Expressed as quantity of cells in the top phase (% of total cells added).

glycol systems which we have studied, the pH and temperature of the phase systems have the following effects on the partition of (red) cells: an increase of pH increases the partition in a given phase system; and an increase of temperature increases the partition. These studies as well as those testing the effect of ionic strength on partition have been published in detail elsewhere (22).

One of the properties of the dextran–polyethylene glycol phase systems that should certainly not be overlooked is its great protective effect on the cells which are partitioned. In a phase system ranging from $0.02M$ Tris-H_2SO_4 to $0.42M$ Tris-H_2SO_4 (i.e., from hypotonic to hypertonic concentrations) there is little lysis of cells over a period of an hour or more. However, increasing the tonicity of the phase system leads to a decreased partition of the erythrocytes possibly reflecting the crenation they undergo (Table IV).

In conclusion, we have illustrated the usefulness of partition studies with cells. Variables that affect partition include: the kind and quantity of the polymers, the composition of the salts (both cations and anions), the charge of the particle or cell to be partitioned, the pH, temperature, ionic strength and, in the case of the red cell, the tonicity. In addition to these, substantial numbers of additional factors will probably be found on further study.

So far, partition has enabled us to test for alterations in surface characteristics which occur as a function of age, storage, chemical nature of surface charge components, and chemical modification of cell membranes. Differences in the partition between reticulocyte polysomes and monosomes have also recently been found, but the basis for this difference has not as yet been elucidated.

TABLE IV

Effect of Increasing Tonicity of Phase Systems on the Partition of Human Red Blood Cells [a]

Tris-H_2SO_4	Partition [b]
$0.02M$	94
$0.12M$	95
$0.18M$	92
$0.21M$	60
$0.30M$	19
$0.42M$	9

[a] Phase systems contained 5% (w/w) dextran, 4% (w/w) polyethylene glycol and the indicated molarity of Tris-H_2SO_4 buffer (pH 7.5).
[b] Expressed as the quantity of cells in the top phase (% of total cells added).

APPENDIX ON PROCEDURE

The following brief outline presents some of the basic procedures used in our laboratory to partition cells and to do countercurrent distribution experiments with cells in dextran–polyethylene glycol two-phase systems. For a more extensive coverage of these and additional points of procedure see references 5, 7, 10, 11, 19–21, and, especially, reference 9.

Preparation of Stock Solutions

A. Dextran. Dextran 500 (Pharmacia Fine Chemicals, Uppsala, Sweden) is hygroscopic. A 20% (w/w) stock solution is prepared by weighing out approximately 220 g of the dextran and making it up to 1000 g with water. The dextran dissolves slowly (even without heating) but it is advisable to heat the final solution at 90–95° C for 15 min. Dextran solutions prepared in this way can usually be kept in the cold for periods up to 3 or 4 weeks. Without heating, microbiological contamination takes place much faster. An aliquot of the dextran stock solution diluted five-fold with water is taken for polarimetric measurement, $[a]_D^{25} = +199°$. The exact percent (w/w) is then calculated and recorded. When 220 g are made up to 1000 g with water, the dextran solution will be in the neighborhood of 20% (w/w).

B. DEAE–dextran. DEAE–dextran (Pharmacia) is made up in a manner similar to that indicated above. However, the $[a]$ depends on the degree of substitution of the dextran and must first be determined for the particular batch with which one works. DEAE–dextran comes with a small quantity of dialyzable NaCl, which is usually not enough to affect the partition of *cells*.

C. Polyethylene glycol. PEG (obtained from Union Carbide, Los Angeles, as Carbowax 6000) does not take up water. Forty percent (w/w) stock solutions are prepared by simply weighing out 400 g of PEG and making it up to 1000 g with water. Such a solution can be stored almost indefinitely in the coldroom. We have found PEG (solid) to turn yellow on extended storage. This has not been found to affect the partition of cells, however.

D. Salt solutions. Salt and buffer solutions that are a convenient number of times more concentrated than the desired concentration in the phase system are prepared in the usual manner. Thus, in most of our work we have used stock solutions containing 0.60M NaCl; 0.44M Na-phosphate buffer (composed of equimolar parts of mono- and dibasic phosphates), etc.

H. WALTER

Preparation of Phase Systems

The first thing to decide on is the quantity of a desired phase system that one wishes to prepare. If one wishes to prepare 50 g of a phase system containing (as an example): 5% (w/w) dextran, 4% (w/w) PEG, 0.1% DEAE–D, 0.15M NaCl, and 0.01M Na-phosphate buffer, one has to calculate the dilutions needed of the available stock solutions into 50 g of phase to obtain the desired system.

Available stocks	Amount needed (for above phase system)
18.94% (w/w) dextran	13.20 g
40% (w/w) PEG	5.00
9.97% (w/w) DEAE–D	0.50
0.60M NaCl	12.50
0.44M Na-phosphate buffer	1.14
H$_2$O	17.66

Total: 50.00 g

The mixture is shaken extremely well and may be stored in the cold for periods up to about three weeks. It can be frozen and kept indefinitely. If kept at 5°C it must be periodically examined for evidence of microbiological contamination. If any contamination is evident, the phase system must be discarded and fresh phases prepared. The removal of contaminants is not adequate prior to use of phases since, after contamination, the composition of the phase system is indeterminate. The author has observed contaminants which can rapidly break down dextran and, in a matter of hours, convert a two-phase system into a single phase.

Partition Experiments

The phases must be at the temperature at which partition is to be carried out. They are then shaken vigorously and poured rapidly into calibrated test tubes of uniform diameter. The phases are permitted to settle and the volume of the top phase is recorded. (For phase systems in which the volumes of the top and bottom phases are very different, enough top or bottom phase is withdrawn to make the top and bottom phase volumes approximately equal). It is both of interest and importance to point out that the partition of cells in dextran–polyethylene glycol phase systems is *independent* of phase volumes. Thus, if the top phase volume is doubled, the cell concentration will be halved and the *total* percent of cells found in the top phase will be the same. However, as changes in the relative phase volumes affect the settling time, it is of advantage to run partition experiments in phase systems in which the top and bottom phase volumes are essentially equal.

A small volume of washed packed cells (not exceeding 1% of the total phase volume) is pipetted both into the phase system and into another (empty) tube. The phase system containing the cells is inverted for mixing a number of times (e.g., 20) and is then permitted to settle for a period of time by the clock. Twenty minutes is usually adequate if the partition is run in tubes in the vertical position. Five to eight minutes is sufficient if the tubes are capped and permitted to settle in perfectly horizontal position. After this time 1 ml of top phase is carefully withdrawn from the top phase (about halfway down in the top phase for greater reproducibility). The cell concentration is then analyzed either directly (e.g., by reading on a Klett photoelectric colorimeter) or by lysing the cells (in the case of red cells) followed by removal of stromal material and measurement of the hemoglobin absorbance. The reading is recalculated for dilution and total top phase volume. It is related to the aliquot pipetted into the phase system (after analyzing the sample that was pipetted into the second tube at the same time). Data are expressed as the quantity of cells in the top phase (percent of total cells added).

Countercurrent Distribution

The best way to do countercurrent distribution experiments with cells is to set up the apparatus in a circular manner so that the last tube is connected to the first and all tubes are filled with both top and bottom phases. In this way problems arising from incomplete settling of phases are avoided and cocurrent attachments are not necessary. It is further of great advantage to use a thin-layer countercurrent apparatus for polymer two-phase systems (11). Since the settling time is dependent, among other things, on the height of the phase column, using a "thin-layer" apparatus as described by Albertsson vastly decreases the settling time. This is not only useful because of the saving in time, but can be essential in the case of cells which cannot be subjected to countercurrent distribution for a period of 20 or more hours. With the thin-layer unit, approximately twice as many transfers can be accomplished in half the time. If a thin-layer unit is not available, a standard Craig-Post apparatus can be used with the extraction tubes placed in perfectly horizontal position during the settling part of the cycle (19). In this manner one can simulate the thin-layer apparatus and derive the benefits of more rapid settling times for the phase systems.

144   H. WALTER

In loading the apparatus one has to decide at the start what one wishes to do with the interface (10). When partitioning cells, some will always accumulate at the interface (9), and the decision to be made is whether the cells at the interface are to be treated as part of the top or as part of the bottom phase. We have always treated the cells at the interface as part of the bottom phase. This means that in loading a countercurrent apparatus with, for example, a bottom phase capacity of 1 ml, only 0.9 ml of bottom phase is placed into each tube or cavity (except the "load tubes") thereby assuring that the cells at the interface will not be transferred. Then, 1.1 ml of top phase is placed into each tube except the "load tubes." The "load tubes" are those tubes that are also to be loaded with the cells. In general we have loaded up to 5 tubes for 50 and 10 tubes for 120 transfers with cells. The load tubes receive the same amount of top phase as the other tubes, up to 10% of the phase volume of packed cells, and bottom phase volume is equal to that of the other tubes *minus* the cell volume used. *As an example:* when the tubes are filled with 0.9 ml bottom phase and 1.1 ml top phase, the load tubes can be filled with 0.7 ml bottom phase, 0.2 ml packed cells, and 1.1 ml top phase. In those cases where the packed cells cannot be pipetted they must be suspended in phase (e.g., top) for pipetting purposes.

Countercurrent distribution is then carried on in the usual manner, using 20–25 min as the settling time when settling is with the tubes in the vertical position, and about 5–8 min when in the horizontal position. At the end, the extraction tubes are emptied, the cells centrifuged down, and the supernatant phases discarded. The cells are then suspended in a desired liquid (e.g., saline, or water for lysing, etc.) for analysis. With some cells difficulty is encountered when attempting to centrifuge them down from undiluted phases. In such cases one must dilute the phase system with saline prior to centrifugation. This gives rise to a single phase.

Acknowledgments

I express my appreciation to Robert P. Coyle, Romulo Garza, Eugene J. Krob, Fred W. Selby, and Royce Winge for technical assistance. These investigations were supported in part by a Grant from the National Heart Institute, United States Public Health Service (Grant HE 08304).

References

1. H. Walter, F. W. Selby, and J. M. Brake, *Biochem. Biophys. Res. Commun.,* **15,** 497 (1964).
2. H. Walter and F. W. Selby, *Biochim. Biophys. Acta,* **112,** 146 (1966).

3. H. Walter, R. Garza, and F. W. Selby, *Exptl. Cell Res.*, **49**, 679 (1968).
4. H. Walter, R. Winge, and F. W. Selby, *Biochim. Biophys. Acta*, **109**, 293 (1965.)
5. H. Walter, F. W. Selby, and R. Garza, *Biochim. Biophys. Acta*, **136**, 148 (1967).
6. H. Walter and R. P. Coyle, *Biochim. Biophys. Acta*, **165**, 540 (1968).
7. H. Walter and P.-Å. Albertsson, *Biochem. Biophys. Res. Commun.*, **25**, 670 (1966).
8. H. Walter, E. J. Krob, R. Garza, and G. S. Ascher, *Exptl. Cell Research* (in press).
9. P.-Å. Albertsson, *Partition of Cell Particles and Macromolecules*, Wiley, New York, 1960.
10. P.-Å. Albertsson and G. D. Baird, *Exptl. Cell Res.*, **28**, 296 (1962).
11. P.-Å. Albertsson, *Anal. Biochem.*, **11**, 121 (1965).
12. A. Miller and A. B. Maunsbach, *Science*, **151**, 1000 (1966).
13. M. Bessis and M. Bricka, *Rev. Hematol.*, **7**, 407 (1952).
14. J. G. Stephens, *J. Physiol.*, **99**, 30 (1940).
15. D. Danon and Y. Marikovsky, *Compt. Rend.*, **253**, 1271 (1961).
16. D. A. Haydon and G. V. F. Seaman, *Arch. Biochem. Biophys.*, **122**, 126 (1967).
17. E. H. Eylar, M. A. Madoff, O. V. Brody, and J. L. Oncley, *J. Biol. Chem.*, **237**, 1992 (1962).
18. G. M. W. Cook, personal communication.
19. H. Walter and F. W. Selby, *Biochim. Biophys. Acta*, **148**, 517 (1967).
20. H. Walter, R. Garza, and R. P. Coyle, *Biochim. Biophys. Acta*, **156**, 409 (1968).
21. H. Walter, in *Proceedings of the Protides of Biological Fluids*, XVth Colloquium, H. Peeters, Ed., Elsevier, Amsterdam, 1968, p. 367.
22. H. Walter, E. J. Krob, and R. Garza, *Biochim. Biophys. Acta*, **165**, 507 (1968).

Partition of Nucleic Acids in Polymer Two-Phase System

DAVID E. PETTIJOHN

Department of Biophysics, University of Colorado Medical Center, Denver, Colorado

I. INTRODUCTION

Separations of certain macromolecules or biological particles can sometimes be achieved by a technically simple procedure based upon partition in a polymer phase system. In this chapter the partition properties of several biologically important macromolecules will be discussed and specific fractionation procedures will be presented to illustrate the application of the phase systems.

Several different polymer phase systems have been described by Albertsson (1). Of these the polyethylene glycol–dextran system has had the most extensive application; the discussion here will therefore

147

emphasize this system. Furthermore, this section will treat the fractionation of macromolecules and molecular complexes. Separations of cell particles by phase-system partition is described in the preceding chapter by Walter.

A. The Polyethylene Glycol–Dextran System

If one mixes together aqueous solutions of polyethyelene glycol (PEG) and dextran at the appropriate concentrations, a turbid emulsion is formed and upon standing the mixture will separate into two nearly clear phases; the upper and lower phases containing, respectively, the higher concentrations of PEG and dextran. A phase diagram for the PEG–dextran system (1) is given in Figure 1. The curved line (the binodial) shows the transition between phase system and homogeneous solution. Concentrations of PEG and dextran which give points in the area above this curve will give rise to a phase system, while points below the curve will be homogeneous solutions. The parallel lines (tie lines) can be used to predict the compositions and relative volumes of the phases (1). The points of intersection with the right- and left-hand regions of the binodial give the composition of the lower and upper phases, respectively. The ratio of the distances along the tie line from the point representing the total composition to the two intersection points gives the approximate ratio of the volumes of the two phases. Thus the point shown on the upper tie line of Figure 1 was obtained from a mixture of 7.5% dextran with 5.8% PEG w/w and gives rise to a system with an upper phase containing

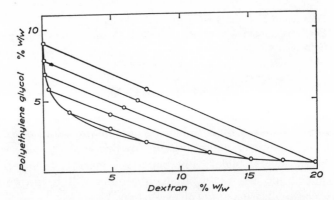

Fig. 1. A phase diagram for the PEG–dextran phase system. The dextran and PEG had weight average molecular weights of 460,000 and 6,000–7,500, respectively. The system was equilibrated at 0°C. (Reproduced from the data of Albertsson (1) by permission of the author.)

0.03% dextran and 9.03% PEG, lower phase 19.9% dextran and 0.55% PEG (w/w) and with an upper phase volume approximately 1.6 times greater than the lower (see reference 1 for a more detailed treatment of the phase diagram).

A substance to be partitioned is added to the PEG–dextran system just before mixing. After equilibration the concentrations of the partitioned substance in the two phases are measured and the partition coefficient, K, is defined as

$$K = \frac{\text{concentration in upper phase}}{\text{concentration in lower phase}}$$

B. Factors Influencing Partition Coefficients

Unfortunately a well-developed theory to explain the partition properties of macromolecules is not available and it is necessary to proceed empirically.

Albertsson (1) has found that the phase diagram of the PEG–dextran system is influenced by both the molecular weights of the PEG and dextran and the temperature at which the system is equilibrated. These factors accordingly also effect the partition of any material introduced into the system. Likewise, the point on the phase diagram at which one operates (i.e., the concentrations of PEG and dextran) strongly affects partition properties (2,7). The useful systems have polymer concentrations which are not far removed from the binodial (2). Another variable which must be vigorously controlled is the ionic composition present in the phase system. The partition coefficient of a particular molecular species is usually dependent upon the buffer that is used and the concentration and chemical nature of any salts that are present. Once defined these ionic effects can frequently be used to advantage in fractionation procedures, as will be illustrated below.

C. Advantages of Fractionation By Partition in a Polymer Phase System

As will be described below, it is sometimes possible to assemble a phase system in which a macromolecule to be separated partitions almost completely into a phase from which other undesirable materials are excluded. This fortunate situation enables a complete fractionation of the macromolecule to be obtained after a few routine extractions. In other cases where only differential partitions are obtained, the advantages are not so clear-cut in terms of simplicity, since countercurrent methods are then required.

The PEG–dextran phase system in its normal use has water contents greater than 85–90% (see Fig. 1). This means that delicate biological structures can be extracted in an aqueous environment and that harsh procedures involving percipitations, absorptions, or treatments with organic reagents can be avoided. Enzyme activities are usually stable in solutions containing the phase system polymers; moreover it has been frequently observed that in solutions containing PEG, enzyme activities are protected against surface denaturation due to shaking or stirring. As will be described below, the gentle conditions of this technique make it applicable to the fractionation of biological aggregates such as enzyme–nucleic acid complexes.

II. METHODS AND MATERIALS

A. Materials

Polyethylene glycol 6000 was purchased from Fluka, Buchs, Switzerland or from Union Carbide, New York; Dextran 500 (batch 852 or 8689) was purchased from Pharmacia, Uppsala, Sweden, (batch 5406 was found unsatisfactory since it contained what was probably a trace of salt and could not be used without further purification). DNA from $E.\ coli$, T_4 phage and polyoma virus were purified as described previously (3,4). RNA polymerase was purified by the method of Chamberlin and Berg (5) with modifications and additional steps as described previously (6).

B. The PEG–Dextran System

Methods for preparing the phase system were those of Albertsson (1,7). A stock solution containing 10% (w/w) dextran 500 and 8% (w/w) PEG 6000 in sterile distilled water was prepared from separate 20% dextran and 30% PEG solutions. After thorough shaking, an aliquot of the stock solution was removed and mixed in a stoppered tube with an equal weight of a suitably buffered solution containing the material to be partitioned. Except where specifically noted, the final system in the work described here was 5% dextran, 4% PEG w/w. Dextran and PEG solutions were dispensed by weighing, since volumetric delivery is inaccurate due to viscosity. All operations were at 4°C; final mixing was done by repeated inversion of the tube. Low-speed centrifugation brought the system to equilibrium in a few minutes; the top phase contained most of the PEG and had a volume about equal to the dextran-rich lower phase. Partition coefficients (K) were measured from either ultraviolet absorption, enzyme activities, or radioactivities associated with the partitioned substances.

C. Buffers

The sodium phosphate buffers which were used in the PEG–dextran phase system all had final phosphate concentrations of $0.01M$ and the ratio NaH_2PO_4/Na_2HPO_4 was varied in particular experiments as described in the text. Buffer A had a ratio of 7.0/3.0; other ratios are indicated by this same convention.

III. PARTITION OF MACROMOLECULES

A. Nucleic Acids

The partition properties of the various classes of nucleic acid in the PEG–dextran system are usually quite distinct. Likewise, topological and structural variants of certain species of DNA have been found to partition differently. As an example, shown in Figure 2 is the change in partition coefficient which occurs when DNA is heated beyond the temperature at which strand separation occurs. This effect which has been known for some years now (8) can be readily exploited to obtain separation of double- and single-stranded DNA.

The influence of the sodium phosphate buffer ratio on the partition coefficients of different nucleic acids in the PEG–dextran system. is

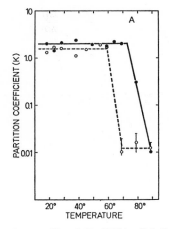

Fig. 2. Heat denaturation profile of T_4 DNA. Solutions containing approximately 0.1 µg ^{3}H-labeled T_4 DNA in 0.40 ml $0.02M$ sodium phosphate buffer pH 6.4 were heated for 5 min in water baths at the indicated temperatures. In one series of tubes 1% formaldehyde was included. The solutions were cooled on crushed ice, additional cold buffer with or without 1% formaldehyde was added and the DNA was partitioned in the PEG–dextran system. When used the final formaldehyde concentration in the phase system was 0.5%. (○) Heated and analyzed with formaldehyde. (●) Without formaldehyde.

shown in Figure 3. The data illustrate both the significant differences in partition of these nucleic acids and also the importance of the buffer ratio in determining the absolute value of the partition coefficients. In designing a procedure for the fractionation of nucleic acids it is obviously important to choose the correct sodium phosphate buffer. For instance, in separating DNA from high molecular weight *E. coli* RNA a system containing 5mM NaH_2PO_4 and 5mM Na_2HPO_4 will partition the two primarily into different phases, while a buffer ratio significantly higher or lower than this brings the two nucleic acids into the same phase. It should be emphasized that the addition of salts or other buffers to the phase system usually alters the profile shown in Figure 3. For example, when 0.02M NaCl is present, the

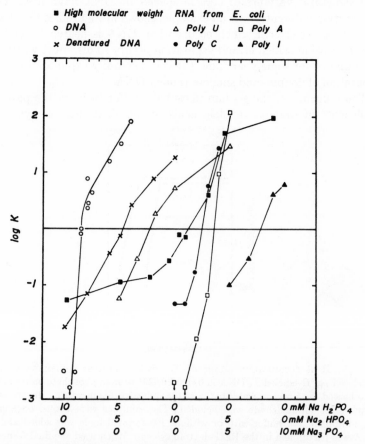

Fig. 3. Partition of different nucleic acids in the PEG–dextran system. (From the data of Albertsson (7) by permission of the author.)

curves shown in Figure 3 are shifted far to the right (see Table V). Albertsson (1,7) has found that the general rule for ionic effects is that divalent anions such as HPO_4^{2-} or SO_4^{2-} give higher partition coefficients while monovalent anions such as the halides lower the K values in the order $F^- < Cl^- < I^- < Br^-$. Alkaline chlorides reduce the K values in the order $Li^+ < Na^+ < Cs^+ < K^+$. The overall effects of different ions are additive and are dependent on relative concentrations. If higher ionic strengths are required in the system, moderate amounts of ammonium sulfate (up to approximately $0.10M$) can be added without greatly altering the partition of DNA from the values shown in Figure 3. Also mixtures of lithium and sodium chloride at concentrations of $0.1M$, have been used successfully with phosphate buffers.

The influence of the molecular weight of a macromolecule on its partition in the PEG–dextran system has not been studied in detail. It has, however, been observed that nucleic acids of low molecular weights such as s-RNA partition with K values near 1 even in the presence of different buffers or salt concentrations (7,8). (Also see Table V below.) This effect is in qualitative agreement with the Brønsted relationship (9,10).

$$K = e^{\lambda M / kt}$$

where K is the partition coefficient, M the molecular weight of the partitioned molecule, k the Boltzmann constant, t the temperature, and λ a constant characteristic of the phase system and the partitioned molecule. Evidently this equation does not hold for high molecular weight DNA. As shown in Table I unfragmented T_4 DNA and large $E.$ $coli$ DNA molecules partition with lower K values than do smaller fragments of these same DNAs produced by shear. Because of this effect the difference in partition coefficient between single- and double-stranded DNA is not as great for very large DNA molecules as it is for smaller fragments.

It is possible to prepare double-stranded DNA molecules containing regions of partial denaturation by carrying out a limited reaction of the DNA with formaldehyde (11,12). Such preparations contain no completely single-stranded molecules detectable by banding in CsCl gradients (3). As shown in Figure 4, the partition coefficients of such partially denatured DNA are significantly reduced from those of more perfectly helical molecules. Linear DNA molecules containing only about 10% denaturation have K values about 10-fold removed from untreated DNA; while those molecules containing more than 60% denaturation partition as completely denatured DNA. These

154   D. E. PETTIJOHN

TABLE I

Partition Coefficients of DNA of Different Molecular Weights [a]

DNA	Mol wt (approx.)	minus formaldehyde		plus formaldehyde	
		Unheated	Heated quick chilled	Unheated	Heated quick chilled
E. coli	10×10^6	25	0.04	25	0.06
E. coli	50×10^6	1.8	—	1.9	0.01
T₄	130×10^6	2.3	0.01	2.5	0.01
T₄	5×10^6	>100	—	60	0.005
Polyoma I	3.2×10^6	30	—	30	0.59
Polyoma II	3.2×10^6	>70	—	65 (approx.)	0.02

[a] Radioactive DNA in $0.02M$ buffer A with or without 1.0% formaldehyde was either kept at 4°C or heated 84°–90°C and returned to 4°C. The DNA was then analyzed in the PEG–dextran system. When formaldehyde was used, its final concentration in the phase system was 0.5%. The mol wt of the DNA was estimated by sedimentation (14).

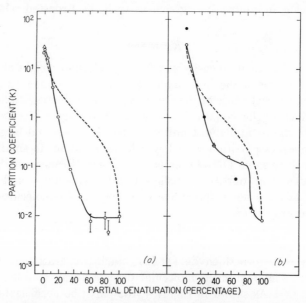

Fig. 4. Partition of partially denatured DNA. The DNA was prepared by partial reaction with formaldehyde. The extent of denaturation was defined by hyperchromicity and by buoyant density in CsCl density gradients (3). The dashed line represents the function expected if a partially denatured DNA ($x\%$) partitions as a mixture of $x\%$ completely denatured and $(100-x\%)$ completely helical molecules. (a) E. coli DNA (○) (b) Polyoma DNA; (○) Form I; (●) Form II.

properties can be of use in eliminating or selecting partially denatured DNA molecules (arising, for example, from frayed or unpaired ends) from DNA preparations (2,4).

Partition in the PEG–dextran system is also a means for distinguishing supercoiled DNA molecules (13) from DNA lacking this topology. As shown in Table II the partition coefficients of supercoiled (form I) polyoma DNA are 6- to 12-fold smaller than those of the open circle and linear forms II and III. This partition difference may arise from the more compact configuration of the supercoiled DNA relative to the open circle and linear forms or from the partially uncoiled helical structure which may exist in form I DNA (13).

B. Proteins

Most proteins partition in the PEG–dextran system with rather similar K values not far removed from unity. This condition is maintained with only minor changes in different buffers and with the addition of moderate amounts of different salts. (See Table V or reference 1 for a few examples.) For this reason the phase system technique has no particular advantage at this stage of its development in separating different proteins. However, these same properties make the phase system useful in separating nucleic acids and protein–nucleic acid complexes from proteins. Applications of this type will be discussed below.

In the presence of high concentrations of NaCl proteins *do* attain partition coefficients significantly greater than unity (1) (Fig. 5). Since high molecular weight nucleic acids have very small K values in the presence of significant NaCl concentrations (see Table V for an example), this system can be readily applied to obtain efficient separa-

TABLE II

Partition of Polyoma DNA I, II, III [a]

Mixture	K_{14C}	K_{3H}	K_{32P}	K_{II}/K_I	K_{III}/K_I	K_{III}/K_{II}
1. ³H-I + ¹⁴C-II	5.4	0.56		9.5		
2. ¹⁴C-I + ³H-III	1.02	12.0			12.0	
3. ³H-I + ¹⁴C-III	8.6	0.73			12.0	
4. ¹⁴C-II + ³H-III	1.2	2.9				2.5
5. ³²P-II + ³H-III		1.1	0.75			1.5

[a] Radioactive polyoma DNA was equilibrated in the PEG–dextran system containing the following sodium phosphate buffer ratios: mixture 1, 8.50/1.50; mixtures 2 and 3, 8.75/1.25; mixtures 4 and 5, 9.00/1.00.

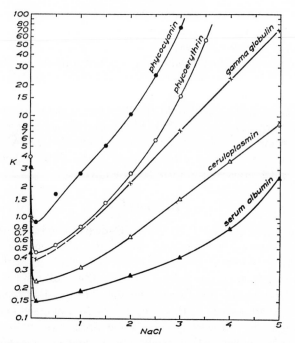

Fig. 5. Partition of different proteins in the PEG–dextran system containing increasing concentrations of NaCl. The salt concentrations are in moles added per kg phase system solutions. (From the data of Albertsson (7) by permission of the author.)

tions of nucleic acid from protein. It has been used as a first step in the purification of DNA polymerase (15), RNA polymerase (16) and DNA (17) from bacteria. A convenient system for this protein–nucleic acid separation is 6.5% w/w dextran 500, 2.0% w/w PEG 6000, and 5 moles NaCl per kg phase system (1).

C. Protein–DNA Complex

Shown in Table III are the partition coefficients of DNA in the presence of varied concentrations of different proteins. At the ionic strength and pH which was used bovine serum albumin does not form a complex with the DNA while the other proteins and polyamines do (3). The DNA concentrations in these mixtures were kept low (less than 0.1 μg/ml) to avoid percipitation effects. The data show that a noninteracting protein such as the serum albumin does not influence the partition of DNA. Likewise, several proteins which form complexes with DNA such as lysozyme, RNase or protamine do not

TABLE III

Ratio of the Partition Coefficient of DNA with Protein to That of Free DNA [a]

0.05 μg ³H-labeled DNA plus	Protein added (μg)			
	1.0	10	50	100
Bovine serum albumin	1	2	1	
Lysozyme	1.2	3	3	2
RNase	1	0.5	0.7	
Protamine		4	2	1
Spermidine	1	0.5	0.2	
Chymotrypsin		0.1	10^{-3}	$<10^{-4}$
Chrymotrypsin + 200 μg E. coli DNA				1.5
RNA polymerase HA-1	0.06	0.001		
RNA polymerase (heated)		0.8		

[a] *Escherichia coli* ³H-labeled DNA was mixed with the proteins or polyamines shown above in buffer A and brought to equilibrium in the PEG–dextran system. The K value of the DNA was compared to that of the DNA without protein.

significantly affect the K value of the DNA. By contrast, the complex with chymotrypsin or RNA polymerase partitions differently from the free DNA. This change is dependent on the ratio of enzyme to DNA not on the absolute concentration of enzyme and the effect is abolished if the enzyme solution is heated before adding the DNA.

Figure 6 shows in more detail the partition of the RNA polymerase–

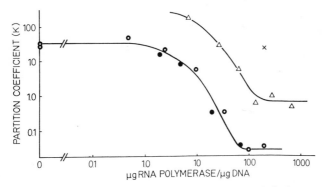

Fig. 6. Partition of RNA polymerase–DNA complexes. Solutions containing 0.05 μg radioactive *E. coli* DNA were mixed with varying amounts of RNA polymerase to give the above ratios and brought to equilibrium in the PEG–dextran system. The phase system also contained: (○) only buffer A; (●) buffer A plus 250 μg/ml BSA; (△) sodium phosphate buffer 4.0/6.0 plus 250 μg/ml BSA; (✕) enzyme inactivated by heating at 95°.

158   D. E. PETTIJOHN

DNA complex. At low ratios of the enzyme to DNA (less than about 1 µg polymerase/µg DNA) the complex partitions as free DNA, while at a ratio of about 100 µg/µg DNA the K value is at a minimum of approximately 10^{-3} times the value of free DNA. At this minimum the DNA is apparently saturated by RNA polymerase since further additions of the polymerase do not effect the partition of the complex. This saturation point agrees with the value at which sedimentation rates of the RNA polymerase–DNA complex reach on upper limit (6). At the low ionic strengths used in this phase system, the RNA polymerase attaches nonspecifically and at a ratio of 100/1 the DNA is essentially covered by enzyme (6).

At saturation the polymerase–DNA complex partitions differently from either the free DNA or the free polymerase (Table V). It is interesting, however, that even in different sodium phosphate buffers the K values of the saturated complex are very similar to those of the denatured DNA (Fig. 7). The chymotrypsin–DNA complex partitions differently from denatured or double-stranded DNA.

The partition properties of the RNA polymerase–DNA complex which are described here seem favorable for several types of fractionations. An example of one such application, the extraction of RNA polymerase–DNA complex from bacterial extracts, is described below (IV. B).

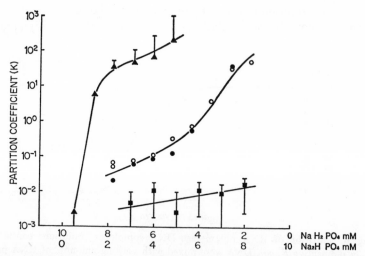

Fig. 7. Variation of partition coefficients with the sodium phosphate buffer ratio: (▲) *E. coli* DNA; (○) *E. coli* DNA heat denatured; (●) *E. coli* DNA with RNA polymerase, 150 µg enzyme/µg DNA; (■) *E. coli* DNA with chymotrypsin, 3.0 mg enzyme/µg DNA.

D. Removal of Phase Polymers

PEG can be removed from nucleic acid solutions by extracting with chloroform (17). In cases where the nucleic acid is obtained in the bottom, dextran-rich phase, it can be transferred to the PEG phase by adding NaOH (see Fig. 3) and then this phase can be treated with chloroform.

Another method for eliminating the PEG involves mixing dry potassium phosphate into the PEG-containing solution. At the proper PEG and phosphate concentrations, a new phase system is formed with the PEG in one phase and potassium phosphate solution in the other (1,2). In this system proteins and nucleic acids partition into the salt solution phase. It is also possible to add CsCl directly to PEG-containing solutions and to form CsCl density gradients from the resultant solution. The PEG is "salted out" and floats on top of such a gradient (2). Likewise, the PEG-rich phase can be layered directly onto a 5–20% w/v sucrose gradient and fast-sedimenting proteins and nucleic acids can be sedimented free of the phase polymer.

IV. APPLICATIONS

As a first step in designing a fractionation procedure with the PEG–dextran system, it is necessary to select the composition of the phase mixture and to calibrate the K values of the components to be separated in this system. The 5% dextran, 4% PEG mixture is useful for many macromolecules; however, different concentrations of the phase polymers may be preferable in some cases (2). Curves such as those described in Figures 3 and 7 should be obtained for the major molecular components to be fractionated. These figures should be reestablished whenever new batches of dextran or PEG are introduced since the molecular weights (and occasional salt contents) of these polymers are variable.

A. Isolation of Denatured DNA from a Bacterial Lysate

A small amount of denatured DNA has been found to occur in bacterial extracts in which the DNA has been fragmented by shear (4). The following simple procedure gives a complete separation of this minority fraction from an excess of double-stranded DNA.

A thymine-requiring mutant of *E. coli* was grown for many generations with ^{3}H-thymidine, the cells collected by centrifugation and washed thoroughly by resuspension and centrifugation in a buffer–salt mixture ($0.05M$ $(NH_4)_2SO_4$, $1mM$ EDTA, and $0.05M$ Tris-SO_4

pH 8.0), selected not to interfere with the partition of DNA in the PEG–dextran system. Finally the cells were resuspended in a 1/10 dilution of this solution and lysed with lysozyme. After centrifugation to eliminate cell debris, PEG–dextran stock solutions and sodium phosphate buffer were mixed with the lysate to give a system containing 5% dextran, 4% PEG and $3mM$ Na_2HPO_4, $7mM$ NaH_2PO_4. After equilibration the upper phase containing double helical DNA was removed and the lower phase was extracted four more times with fresh upper phases of identical composition to the first. Aliquots of the final upper and lower phases were assayed for radioactivity. An aliquot of the pooled upper-phase extractions was mixed in fresh PEG–dextran to determine its K value. The results are given in Table IV.

Approximately 2% of the DNA remained in the lower phase of the extraction tube. The K value of this DNA was close to the value of denatured DNA (0.04). The actual amount of denatured DNA in the lysate would be slightly greater than 2% since small losses are expected into the upper phase extractions. The denatured fraction prepared in this way was free of detectable double-stranded DNA. As shown in Figure 8, in a CsCl gradient the separated ^{3}H-DNA forms a band at a higher density than that of double-stranded DNA and there is little, if any, ^{3}H with the double-stranded DNA marker.

Other procedures have also been successful in adapting the PEG–dextran system for routine separations of small amounts of double-stranded from a large excess of single-stranded DNA (18,19).

B. Purification of DNA or Protein–DNA Complex from Bacterial Extracts

Table V shows the K values of several different nucleic acids and proteins in the presence of three different buffers (systems A, B, and C) which are used in this extraction procedure. The technique described here was designed to isolate only the protein–DNA complexes which partition like free DNA, hence the same procedure can be used for

TABLE IV

Denatured DNA in a Bacterial Lysate

	Upper phase, counts/min- 0.10 ml	Lower phase, counts/min- 0.10 ml	K	Total DNA, counts/min	Percentage of total
Extraction tube	36	585	0.06	11,000	2.0
Pooled upper extractions	6,100	745	8.2	550,000	98.0

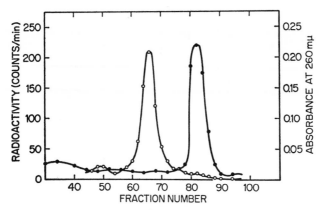

Fig. 8. Equilibrium sedimentation of DNA in an alkaline CsCl gradient. ³H-labeled DNA from the lower phase of the extraction tube of Table IV was mixed with a large excess of nonradioactive double-stranded *E. coli* DNA and brought to equilibrium in a CsCl gradient containing $0.1M$ K_2HPO_4 pH 10.8. Increasing density is to the left. (○) Radioactivity. (●) Absorbance.

purification of DNA. In purifying DNA the extract is first treated to disrupt the protein–DNA complexes, while this step is omitted when purifying complexes.

The procedure consists of the following steps:

1. Careful washing and resuspension of *E. coli* cells by the same process used in the isolation of denatured DNA (see section IV. A).

2. Lysis or disruption of the bacteria by lysozyme or grinding with glass beads (4). Lysis with SDS (sodium dodecyl sulfate, 0.2 to 1.0%) was also used in preparing DNA, but SDS disrupts protein–DNA complexes and must be avoided in that preparation.

3. In purifying DNA the lysate was extracted once by mixing on a rotary mixer at 0–4° with an equal volume of 8 to 1 chloroform-octanal to denature proteins and disrupt protein–DNA complexes. If SDS lysis was used, 2 or 3 chloroform extractions were necessary to reduce SDS concentrations to a level where there was no interference with the PEG–dextran system. The chloroform extraction was avoided in preparing protein–DNA complex, but it was necessary to shear the high molecular weight DNA from lysozyme lysates in order to obtain the high K values of the complex shown for systems A and B of Table V. This was accomplished by stirring the lysate at 0–4° on the same vortex mixer that was used with the chloroform extraction. When cells were disrupted by grinding with glass beads, fragmentation of the DNA was sufficient without further treatment.

4. To the upper aqueous phase of the chloroform extraction or to

TABLE V

Partition Coefficients in the PEG–Dextran System

Final phase system 5% dextran + 4% PEG + the following buffers	Nucleic acids						Proteins		
	E. coli nDNA[a]	E. coli dDNA[b]	High mol wt RNA[c]	Low mol wt RNA[d]	E. coli[e] protein	RNA polymerase	Deoxyribonuclease	Lysozyme	Trypsin
A 3mM Na$_2$HPO$_4$ 7mM NaH$_2$PO$_4$	25	0.04	<0.04	0.8	1.3	2.0	1.0	0.65	0.34
B 5mM NaH$_2$PO$_4$ 5mM Na$_2$HPO$_4$	100	0.3	approx. 0.10	1.0	approx. 2				
C B + 0.02M NaCl	<0.005			0.3	0.7				

[a] E. coli DNA extracted by the method described here.
[b] The same DNA as in footnote a above, heated to 100° for 5 min in buffer A and quick chilled.
[c] Measured with E. coli ribosomal RNA and a pulse labeled RNA from T$_4$ infected cells.
[d] Yeast tRNA.
[e] Ribosome free protein from an E. coli extract labeled with [^{3}H]-arginine.

the stirred lysate from step *3*, sodium phosphate buffer was added to a final concentration of twice that of buffer A. This was then mixed with an equal weight of PEG–dextran stock to give system A of Table V. The salt and buffer which were introduced during the washing (step *1*) were selected to have negligible effect on the K values of Table V.

5. After equilibration the upper phase of system A which contains the DNA or the protein–DNA complex was removed and reequilibrated four more times against twice its volume of a lower phase from system B. These steps remove the large RNA molecules, any denatured DNA and most of the small RNA and free protein.

6. The resultant upper phase from the last extraction of step *5* was then mixed with 1/3 its volume of a fresh lower phase from system B containing 0.08M NaCl. The mixture then has very nearly the buffer–salt concentration of system C and the DNA or protein–DNA complex partitions into the lower phase. The resultant lower phase was then extracted three more times against 3× its volume of upper phase from system C.

7. The final lower phase from step *6* was equilibrated with two to four changes of equal volumes of upper phase from system B to bring the purified DNA or complex back to the upper phase. The upper phases containing the purified product were located by radioactivity or UV absorption measurements.

To prepare for the above extractions large amounts of the systems B and C were made up in advance. After equilibration the upper phases were separated from the lower and held in reserve, to be added as required in steps *5*, *6*, and *7*. When the phases differ in volume as in steps *5* and *6*, the extractions are more efficient and the K values do not differ greatly from those shown in Table V.

Figure 9 records two different extractions in which DNA or protein–DNA complex were purified in parallel from equal fractions of the same lysate. The lower phases of extraction numbers 1 to 5 and upper phase of numbers 6 to 10 contained the RNA, free protein and any denatured DNA and were discarded. The purified DNA or the protein–DNA complex appears in the upper phases of extraction numbers 11 to 13. About 10–20% of the DNA (of bottom Figure 9) remained in the lower phase of the first extraction. Approximately 4% of the double-stranded DNA would normally be expected to partition into this phase (since $K \cong 25$ in system A). In addition a portion of this separated fraction has the characteristics of denatured or partially denatured DNA as described above (see section IV. A). These dena-

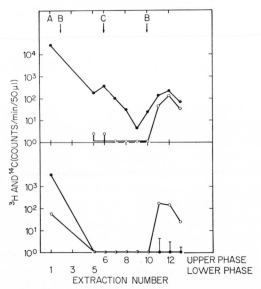

Fig. 9. Purification of protein–DNA complex (top figure) and DNA (bottom figure). *E. coli* TAU-bar grown with C¹⁴-thymine (0.53 mC/mM) and ³H arginine (82 mC/mM) were washed and lysed with lysozyme. Half of the lysate (top figure) was extracted directly for protein-DNA complex as described in the text; the other half (bottom figure) was first treated with chloroform to disrupt the complex. The letters at the top show the points where extractions with systems A, B, and C were begun. During the purification, samples of the upper and lower phases were assayed for radioactivity. (●) ³H; (○) ¹⁴C.

tured fragments were therefore separated from the purified double-stranded DNA.

The DNA preparations which have been obtained by this procedure have been analyzed for protein and RNA contamination by sensitive techniques in which radioactive labels appear in these contaminants (4). The levels of purity are high: $<1\times10^{-3}$mM arginine per millimole DNA-phosphate and $<0.5\%$ ribonuclease-sensitive RNA (4). The DNA had an average molecular weight of 20×10^{6}, determined by sedimentation (14). The recovery of the DNA was normally 30–50% of that introduced into the first polymer phase system. It was estimated from the ratio of ³H to ¹⁴C of Figure 9 that there was about 0.1 mM arginine per millimole DNA–phosphate in the purified protein–DNA complex. A similar complex was extracted from nonradioactive bacteria (4) and the purified complex was analyzed by countercurrent distribution. The result is shown in Figure 10. All the protein and RNA polymerase activity ran with the DNA, in contrast to free pro-

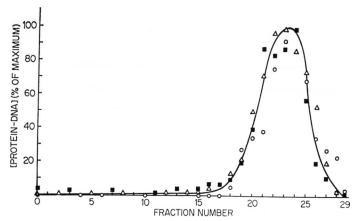

Fig. 10. Countercurrent distribution of protein–DNA complex. A protein–DNA complex was purified by the same procedure as used in Fig. 9, except that non-radioactive bacteria were used and the cells were disrupted by grinding with glass beads in the same buffer used previously plus $3mM$ $MgSO_4$. An aliquot of the purified complex was analyzed in a 30 transfer countercurrent using phase system A. (○) Protein (Lowry) $100\% = 100$ $\mu g/ml$. (△) DNA (E_{260}) $100\% = 190$ $\mu g/ml$. (■) RNA polymerase activity; $100\% = 1.7$ nmole AMP incorporated/ 10 min/ml.

teins which run slower due to their smaller K values. This complex had about 0.5 mg protein per mg DNA. If arginine makes up about one-tenth the weight of the protein in the complex, this figure would agree with that determined by radioactive labeling.

Another method also exists for purifying DNA in the PEG–dextran system (17). This approach utilizes the high-salt system described above, which may have advantages in certain applications.

Acknowledgment

One of the extraction techniques described here was worked out in collaboration with Julliette Favre. A portion of this work was supported by U.S.P.H.S. Research Grant 1 R01 GM 14989–01 and the Damon Runyon Memorial Fund for Cancer Research.

References

1. P. Å. Albertsson, *Partition of Cell Particles and Macromolecules,* Wiley, New York, 1960.
2. B. Alberts, *Biochemistry,* **6,** 2527 (1967).
3. D. Pettijohn, *European J. Biochem,* **3,** 25 (1967).
4. J. Favre and D. E. Pettijohn, *European J. Biochem.,* **3,** 33 (1967).
5. M. Chamberlin and P. Berg, *Proc. Natl. Acad. Sci. U.S.,* **48,** 81 (1962).

6. D. Pettijohn and T. Kamiya, *J. Mol. Biol.*, **29**, 275 (1967).
7. P. Å. Albertsson, *Biochim. Biophys. Acta*, **103**, 1 (1965).
8. P. Å. Albertsson, *Arch. Biochem. Biophys. Suppl.*, **1**, 264 (1964).
9. J. Brønsted, *Z. Physik. Chem. (Bodenstein Festband)*, **1931**, 257.
10. T. Lif, G. Frick, and P. Albertsson, *J. Mol. Biol.*, **3**, 727 (1961).
11. K. I. Berns, and C. A. Thomas, *J. Mol. Biol.*, **3**, 289 (1961).
12. R. Inman, *J. Mol. Biol.*, **18**, 464 (1966).
13. J. Vinograd, J. Lebowitz, R. Radloff, R. Watson, and P. Laipis, *Proc. Natl. Acad. Sci. U.S.*, **53**, 1104 (1965).
14. E. Burgi and A. Hershey, *Biophys. J.*, **3**, 309 (1963).
15. T. Okazaki and A. Kornberg, *J. Biol. Chem.*, **239**, 259 (1964).
16. C. Babinet, *Biochem. Biophys. Res. Commun.*, **26**, 639 (1967).
17. L. Rudin and P. Å. Albertsson, *Biochim. Biophys. Acta*, **134**, 37 (1967).
18. W. Summers and W. Szybalski, *J. Mol. Biol.*, **26**, 107 (1967).
19. B. Alberts and P. Doty, *J. Mol. Biol.*, **32**, 379 (1968).

Equilibrium Density Gradient Separation and Analysis of Lymphocyte Populations *

KEN SHORTMAN

*Walter and Eliza Hall Institute of Medical Research,
Melbourne, Victoria, Australia*

In my other chapter in this volume a methodology is discussed to separate lymphocytes by size. This report will concern a method of more general application, for separating cells according to another physical parameter, namely density. Full technical details are given elsewhere (1). Only questions of methodology and general application will be considered in this chapter. The real test of the procedure, its application to specific immunological problems, is discussed elsewhere (2,3).

I. GENERAL PROBLEMS

There is nothing original in the idea of separating the cells according to fine differences in their buoyant density. Biological materials have been subjected to such procedures since the experiments of Meselson, Stahl, and Vinograd (4), and Leif and Vinograd (5), have shown that erythrocytes can be separated and analyzed in albumin density

* This is publication No. 1238 from The Walter & Eliza Hall Institute of Medical Research, Post Office, Royal Melbourne Hospital, Victoria, Australia. This work was supported by grants from the National Health and Medical Research Council, Canberra, and the Australian Research Grants Committee.

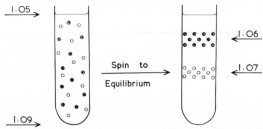

Fig. 1. Schematic representation of the principle of equilibrium density gradient centrifugation. Two types of cells differing in density are dispersed in a linear density gradient. On centrifuging they move up or down to a position corresponding to their buoyant density, at which point the system is in equilibrium and does not change on further spinning.

gradients with a high degree of precision. However, we found there were a number of technical difficulties to be overcome before applying this simple concept to lymphocytes. The principle of the method is shown schematically in Figure 1 and the two major problems to overcome in Figures 2 and 3. In principle, if a mixture of two types of cells is centrifuged in a density gradient, the cells will move up or down until they reach the region corresponding to their buoyant density, and there they will stay, no matter how much longer or harder they are spun. This equilibrium method must be distinguished from a sedimentation rate separation, which might be carried out in a shallower stabilizing gradient, but which would separate according to the rate cells approach the bottom of the tube. This rate would be a function of size, shape, and density, whereas the equilibrium method depends only on cell density.

The first problem to be overcome is that of maintaining a constant

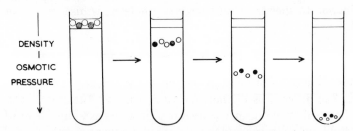

Fig. 2. The problem of maintaining a constant osmotic pressure within the density gradient. The effect of low molecular weight materials such as sucrose, which produce a hypertonic osmotic pressure gradient along with the density gradient. On entering such a gradient cells shrink, increase in density and therefore move further down the gradient where the process continues. Cells eventually sediment out of such a gradient covering their normal density range.

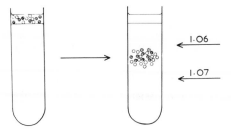

Fig. 3. The problem of aggregation and association. Most high molecular weight media tend to enhance aggregation, and as a result a mixture of two types of cells may band as doublets, triplets and higher aggregates, giving a single broad band of intermediate density.

osmotic pressure within the density gradient. If conventional materials such as sucrose or cesium chloride are used to form a density gradient, they also produce an osmotic pressure gradient. Cells entering such a gradient shrink and increase in density, and this process continues until small, very dense cells reach the bottom of the tube (Fig. 2). This can be overcome by using a high molecular weight substance, which itself makes a negligible osmotic pressure contribution, to produce a density gradient in an isotonic salt solution. We use bovine serum albumin for this purpose. However, this alone does not solve all the osmotic pressure problems and considerable attention must be paid to this aspect. Commercial albumin may have enough salt contaminants to substantially change the osmotic pressure of the medium and therefore must be dialyzed or deionized before use. Freeze-dried albumin may retain enough water to change the osmotic pressure and must therefore be dried over P_2O_5 in a vacuum desiccator before use. Our final medium consists of dialyzed, thoroughly dried, bovine serum albumin (Fraction V, Armour; the powder, not the crystalline product) dissolved in an unbuffered balanced salt solution of 0.294 osmolarity, together with a very small quantity of water (5 ml per 100 g of albumin), to compensate for the small osmotic pressure contribution of the albumin itself.

We have checked that this medium maintains cells at very close to their original volume and density. As far as we can tell from Coulter Counter volume distribution profiles and hematocrit measurements, lymphocytes suspended in this medium maintain the same volume as when suspended in serum. We have used a technique of Danon and Marikovsky (6) to show that the lymphocytes also maintain the same average density as in isologous serum. Rat thymocytes suspended in rat serum were spun in micro hematocrit tubes, each tube containing a small droplet of a mixed oily phthalate ester of known density; after spinning, the position of these density markers above, within, or below the cell sediment served to indicate the density distribution of the population. This gave a value of between 1.066 and 1.068 g/cm^3 for the weight average density of thymic lymphocytes. The corresponding value in our albumin density gradients was from 1.066 to 1.071 g/cm^3. A series of experiments of this type assured us that the physical parameters of the cells were basically unchanged when exposed to our density gradient medium.

The second major problem (Fig. 3) was the tendency of cells to aggregate or associate together, a tendency greatly enhanced by most of the high molecular weight polymers we have tested. This effect may be reduced, but probably not entirely eliminated, in three ways. First, the cells are initially dispersed within the gradient, rather than being applied as a narrow zone at the top. This also prevents the formation of unstable inverse density zones and the resultant streaming and turbulence effects others have noted (7). Second, we chose a medium which minimizes this aggregation effect. If albumin at pH 7.4 is used, marked visible cell aggregation occurs. However, lowering the pH of albumin media reduces this effect until it disappears below pH 5.5. We work at pH 5.1 simply by dissolving albumin in an unbuffered balanced salt solution. The un-neutralized albumin, near its isoelectric point, serves as a very effective buffer in this region. Surprisingly, the cells seem quite unaffected in either their physical parameters or in their biological activity by this low pH. The final way of reducing cell-to-cell interaction is to use a sufficiently high centrifugal force (around 4000g) to oppose this interaction between cells differing in density. This point will be discussed again later.

II. DETAILED PROCEDURE

The following is the detailed actual procedure as performed in our laboratory. All procedures are at 0–4° in a cold room. The steps involved are as follows.

1. Gradient generation. Between 10^7 and 10^9 cells are dispersed in a 13-ml volume linear gradient of albumin (normally from 15–28% w/w) in balanced salt solution, pH 5.1. The gradient generation apparatus is shown in Figure 4. This apparatus, modified from Leif and Vinograd (5), consists of a single mixing chamber, containing initially the dense albumin, with an inlet for the light albumin solution and an outlet for the mixture. A peristaltic pump is used to provide an outlet rate double the input rate, the mathematical conditions for a

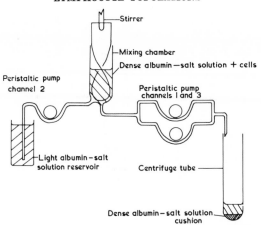

Fig. 4. The gradient generation apparatus. Complete details are given elsewhere (1).

linear density gradient. The gradient is run into a nitrocellulose centrifuge tube containing a small quantity of 40% albumin, to act as
a cushion at the bottom. The cells are initially mixed into the dense
albumin solution. As a result they start off well dispersed within the
gradient, but basically toward the bottom of the tube to avoid their
sedimentation against the cylindrical tube walls when the radial
centrifugal field is applied.

2. Centrifugation. The tube is spun at 4000*g* for 45 min in the
swing-out head of a refrigerated centrifuge. To prevent evaporation
the tube is sealed. The centrifuge is decelerated slowly to reduce
turbulence.

3. Fraction collection. About 30 fractions are collected by upward
displacement of the gradient out of the top of the tube. The fraction
collection apparatus is shown in Figure 5. Fractions are collected
manually on a time basis using a peristaltic pump to displace the
gradient with bromobenzene, pumped in at a constant rate. The
volume of a fraction can be reproduced to within $\pm 1.7\%$ S.D.

4. Density determination. A 3 μl sample of each fraction is then
taken for density determination using a method adapted from Hvidt,
Johansen, Linderstrom-Lang, and Vaslow (8) (Fig. 6). A linear
nonaqueous density gradient covering the region of interest is made
in a sealed 50-ml buret using mixtures of bromobenzene (density
1.49 g/cm³) and petroleum spirit (density 0.79 g/cm³). Three-micro-
liter droplets of each fraction are released from the top of this gradient
and fall till they reach the region corresponding to their own buoyant
density. Their position is read off the buret scale, and the gradient

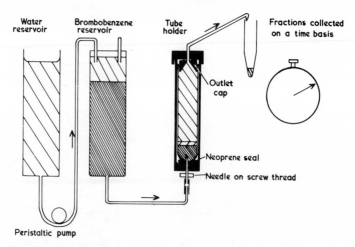

Fig. 5. The fraction collection apparatus. Complete details are given elsewhere (1).

is calibrated with standard albumin solutions, whose density is determined by direct weighing. The standards are stored at $-40°$ as small aliquots in sealed glass ampoules and are used only a few times after opening, to avoid any density drift due to evaporation. With care this

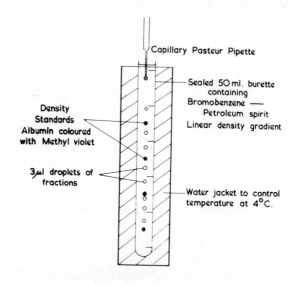

DENSITY   DETERMINATIONS

Fig. 6. Density determination on 3 μl samples of each fraction by the method of Hvidt, Johansen, Linderstrom-Lang, and Vaslow (8), as modified by Shortman (1).

technique allows the density of a fraction to be estimated with a reproducibility of ± 0.00006 g/cm³ S.D.

5. Assay of fractions. Each fraction is then diluted and the cells are spun down and resuspended in a precise volume of buffered balanced salt solution, pH 7.4. The total cell number of each fraction is then determined using a Coulter Counter with a reproducibility of $\pm 0.7\%$ S.D. Other parameters that may be determined for each fraction are biological activity, size range distribution, or morphological distribution.

6. Computing results. Because the density of each fraction is measured with precision, we know that our gradients are not always strictly linear, although an acceptable straightline could be fitted to most of them. Departure from linearity can produce false peaks or troughs in a plot of say, cells-per-fraction against fraction number. To avoid this, all our data are plotted as density distribution functions. This involves calculating, from a plot of mean fraction density against cumulative fraction volume, the density range or density increment covered by each fraction. We can then calculate and plot cells per density increment against density, with all our curves normalized so that the peak value is 100%. To avoid a great many calculations, all the raw data are now routinely entered on IBM cards and computed with an IBM 7044 computer, using a program written by J. Pye and D. Legge.

III. REPRODUCIBILITY OF THE TECHNIQUE

Since we are attempting to use this method as an analytical tool, the precision we can maintain is quite important. In our standard density distribution plots the error in the vertical axis is a composite of errors in density measurement, fraction volume measurement and total cell count, and amounts to an error of $\pm 5\%$ (S.D.) of the value of any particular point. The error in the horizontal axis is simply the error in density measurement and is quite negligible, being about 1/50 of a normal fraction. The reproducibility of the method from one run to another has been assessed in two ways: First, samples of blood were taken from a single individual at intervals over a period of about one month, and the density distribution of the erythrocytes determined. Second, a sample of lymphocytes from a single rat was divided into two lots and subjected to density distribution analysis in two separate runs on the same day. By either method the reproducibility in the position of a peak was the same and amounted to ± 0.0003 g/cm³ S.D., or about one quarter of an average-size fraction.

IV. CELL RECOVERY

An essential requirement was that cells should survive the procedure functionally intact. This requirement has been met, despite the low pH of the medium and the period of centrifugation at 4000g. Over a large number of experiments overall cell recoveries have averaged 89% ± 9% S.D. Recovery of biological activity in a wide range of tests has been around 75% and we have yet to find a system where the procedure causes a marked inactivation of cells. One useful property of the system is that damaged cells, preexistent in the cell suspension or induced by the method itself, tend to spin out of the gradient and accumulate on the dense albumin cushion at the bottom. This is because damaged cells tend to lose cytoplasm, and therefore approach the high density of the nucleus. In regions where the bulk of the cells band, damage is low as judged by the dye exclusion test and the cells appear morphologically in a very good condition.

V. INCREASING RESOLUTION

Although cells may readily be brought to equilibrium in a band by this technique, cell-to-cell interaction and other factors may still reduce the resolution attained. Two experiments using rat thymus cells will be used to show how resolution may be increased. Figure 7 shows

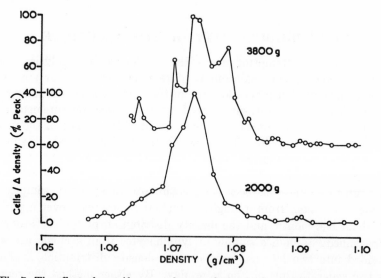

Fig. 7. The effect of centrifuge speed on resolution in the gradient. Two separate samples of 10^8 cells from a single 5-week old male rat thymus were spun at the speeds noted for 90 min in successive runs in 17–34% w/w albumin gradients.

the need for relatively high centrifugal forces, as already mentioned. A sample of cells spun at 2000g gave basically a single peak with a few minor peaks and shoulders. However, a second sample of the same preparation spun at 3800g gave a series of well-defined peaks. This pattern then stayed relatively constant from 4000 up to 9000g. This suggests that the higher centrifugal forces oppose the interaction between cells differing in density. Note also the apparent small increase in number average cell density as the interaction between large, light and small, dense cells is reduced. Figure 8 shows the increase in resolution that may be attained by using only a narrow range gradient, where the entire tube is used to resolve only part of the density span of the cell population. This procedure reduces cell-to-cell interaction and enables more fractions to be cut in a region of closely spaced peaks. As a result a series of clear-cut peaks are resolved where previously only a smear of cells was found.

VI. CONTROL EXPERIMENTS WITH ERYTHROCYTES

Our conclusion from experiments such as these on thymic lymphocytes and other experiments on lymphocytes from lymph nodes, spleen, and thoracic duct lymph is that lymphocyte poulations in general con-

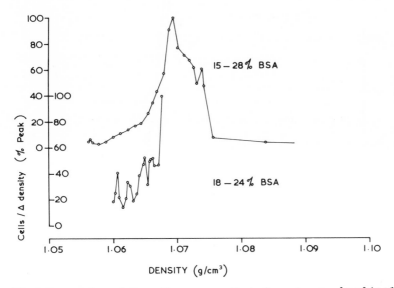

Fig. 8. Increase in resolution with narrow gradients. Separate examples of 4 × 10⁸ cells from a single 8-week old male rat thymus were spun side by side at 4100g for 60 min. The entire centrifuge tube was used to cover the albumin (BSA) ranges noted.

sist of a series of closely spaced but discrete density populations. A series of control experiments described elsewhere (1) provide strong evidence that these peaks are not artifacts of the method. These controls included varying the cell load on the gradient, the centrifuge speed, and the time of centrifugation and also involved a series of experiments where individual fractions were rebanded in a second gradient.

Another way to check the procedure is to deliberately introduce into the system a single population of cells. Erythrocytes would seem to represent a suitable model of a pure cell preparation, and Leif and Vinograd (5) have shown that they form a single band in their gradients. Of course, erythrocytes do vary in density, especially with age, by this only produces a single continuous distribution curve around a characteristic average density, and not a series of peaks. Figure 9 shows that rat erythrocytes also band in our system as a single, fairly sharp peak. However, this will serve to introduce another complication that occurs when dealing with erythrocytes, namely the fact that they swell and band at a relatively low density in the low pH albumin

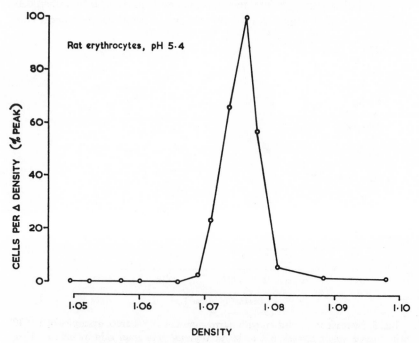

Fig. 9. The density distribution of rat erythrocytes in an albumin gradient at pH 5.4. 3×10^8 cells were centrifuged at $3150g$ for 90 min.

medium. This swelling does not occur with lymphocytes. It is one example of a general phenomenon, the change of erythrocyte volume with pH, that has been described in detail elsewhere (9). In brief, as the pH of the medium is lowered and the ionization of hemoglobin within the red cell changes accordingly, chloride ion enters the red cell in accordance with Gibbs-Donnan equilibria. The resultant change in osmotic pressure causes the cell to swell as the pH is lowered. Thus at pH 5.3 a sample of human erythrocytes banded at density 1.0690, at pH 6.2 at a density of 1.0847, and at pH 7.4 the cells completely spun out of the gradient range and thus had a density greater than 1.1. This has some practical applications, for to attain maximum separation between erythrocytes and lymphocytes it is obviously advisable to work around pH 7, where the erythrocytes will have their maximum density.

VII. VARIABILITY BETWEEN ANIMALS AND STRESS EFFECTS

Although we have been able to establish the reproducibility of the method itself and have some confidence in the validity of the peaks

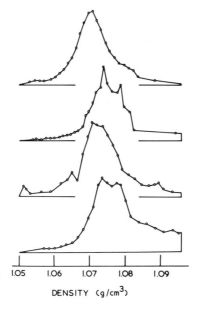

Fig. 10. Variation in the density distribution of 5-week old male Balb C (an inbred strain) mice. The same albumin preparation was used for all experiments, and the upper two curves represent litter mates. The variability is well outside variation due to the method itself ($\pm$ 0.0003 g/cm³ in the position of a peak).

obtained, we have been concerned by the substantial variation in the results obtained between one animal and another. This variation may be obtained even between inbred animals of the same age, and even between litter mates. Such a variation between the density-distribution profile of thymic cells from 5 week male Balb C mice is illustrated in Figure 10. We would appear to be dealing with a variation not only in the average density but also in the number of peaks which are seen. In attempting to find the basis for this we have investigated the effect of corticosteroid hormones on the density-distribution patterns of mouse thymus cells. The thymus is notoriously susceptible to the effects of stress, and corticosteroids are known to have a number of effects on lymphocytes, including the budding off of cytoplasm and eventual cell lysis (10). Figure 11 shows the change in the density distribution of mouse thymic lymphocytes as a function of time after the injection of cortisone acetate, compared to an average curve based

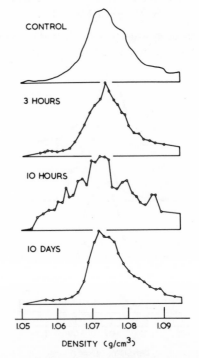

Fig. 11. The effect of corticosteroid administration on the density distribution profile of 5-week old male Balb C mice. The control is a mean of 7 separate runs. The experimental curves are individual, but typical, results at various times after subcutaneous injection of a suspension of 1 mg cortisone acetate. Thymic involution commences 8–10 hr after such treatment, and is complete 24–30 hr later.

on a series of control animals. No change is detectable 3 hr after injection of the hormone but at 10 hr (which is the point when the thymic involution is just beginning), the profile characteristically shows a series of definite peaks. Ten days later, when the thymus has completely involuted and then regenerated to almost normal size, the distribution pattern is now almost back to normal. This suggests that corticosteroid-mediated effects of stress on the animals can cause changes in the thymic lymphocyte density distribution profiles, by directly causing certain changes in the lymphocyte density and also by eliminating certain lymphocytes from the profile. In a series of experiments using adrenalectomized rats, we have obtained simpler, sharper, and more reproducible profiles (11). It may prove necessary to use adrenalectomized animals to simplify analysis of immunological problems by this technique.

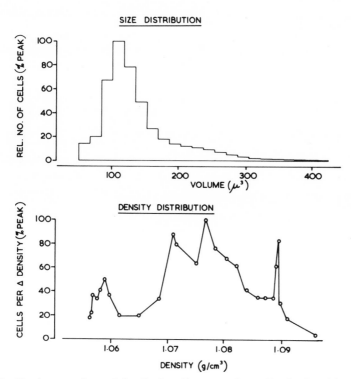

Fig. 12. A comparison of the Coulter Counter volume distribution (9) and the density distribution (1) of the same preparation of 9-week old male rat thymus cells.

VIII. CELL SIZE AND CELL DENSITY

We have tried to determine to what extent lymphocyte buoyant density correlates with other more commonly used parameters such as size or morphological appearance. In fact, our original purpose in designing the method was to separate large, medium, and small lymphocytes. Although the technique should be quite blind to cell size, we argued that cell density should itself vary with the size of the cell.

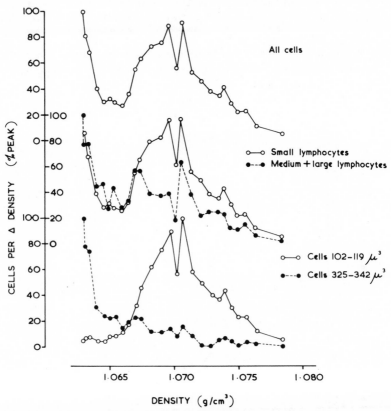

Fig. 13. The density distribution of cells of a given morphological type, or of a closely defined size. All curves are from the same run on 9-week old male rat thymus cells. The upper curve shows the total cell count (obtained with a Coulter Cell Counter). The second curve shows two morphological categories, the total numbers of each category being calculated from total counts and differential counts on smeared and stained samples of each fraction. The lower curve shows the distribution of two size ranges of cells, derived from total cell counts and Coulter Counter volume distribution data, each range representing a single gate of the size distribution plotter.

Thus a small lymphocyte which is predominantly dense cell nucleus should be much more dense than a large lymphocyte which is predominantly cytoplasm. However, a glance at the size distribution and density distribution profiles of the one rat thymus cell preparation (Fig. 12) shows that we cannot be measuring exactly the same parameter. This point can be made more clearly if we follow in the gradient the distribution of cells of a given size or of a given morphological appearance (Fig. 13). In a very general way it is true that large cells tend to be lighter than small cells. However, each conventional morphological class and even a narrowly defined size range of cells is itself heterogeneous and can be resolved into a number of density peaks. If cells of the same size vary in density, we must conclude that those cells vary in their average chemical composition. It seems that the buoyant density of a lymphocyte is determined by the nuclear-to-cytoplasmic ratio as well as by the variable chemical composition of the cell cytoplasm.

References

1. K. Shortman, *Australian J. Expl. Biol. Med. Sci.,* **46,** 375 (1968).
2. K. Shortman, J. S. Haskill, A. Szenberg, and D. G. Legge, *Nature,* **216,** 1227 (1967).
3. J. S. Haskill, *Nature,* **216,** 1229 (1967).
4. M. Meselson, F. Stahl, and J. Vinograd, *Proc. Natl. Acad. Sci. U.S.,* **43,** (1957).
5. R. C. Leif and J. Vinograd, *Proc. Natl. Acad. Sci. U.S.,* **51,** 520 (1964).
6. D. Danon and Y. Marikovsky, *J. Lab. Clin. Med.,* **64,** 668 (1964).
7. S. K. Hilal, D. G. Mosser, M. K. Loken, and R. W. Johnson, *Ann. N.Y. Acad. Sci.,* **114,** 661 (1964).
8. A. Hvidt, G. Johansen, K. Linderstrom-Lang, and F. Vaslow, *Compt. Rend. Trav. Lab. Carlsberg. Ser. Chem.,* **29,** 129 (1954).
9. D. G. Legge and K. Shortman, *Brit. J. Haematol.,* **14,** 323 (1968).
10. T. F. Dougherty, *The Kinetics of Cellular Proliferation,* F. Stohlman, Ed., Grune & Stratton, New York, 1959, p. 264.
11. K. Shortman, in preparation.

Gel Filtration on Agarose Gels

Marius K. Joustra

Pharmacia Fine Chemicals AB, Uppsala, Sweden

Gel filtration, the chromatographic technique whereby substances can be separated according to molecular size and shape, has become one of the classic techniques of biochemistry and has, as such, been comprehensively reviewed (e.g., Determann (1), Gelotte and Porath (2), Joustra (3), Gelotte (4), Granath (5)). Most of the biochemical gel filtration work has been done with crosslinked dextran gels, Sephadex, although also some publication have appeared which describe the use of polyacrylamide gels (6,7).

I. THE LIMITATIONS OF SEPHADEX

Sephadex gels can be successfully used for the fractionation of water-soluble substances up to a molecular weight of ca. 800,000 (compact globular molecules) or ca. 200,000 (randomly coiled chain molecules). The fractionation of molecules and particles of larger dimensions, however, requires a gel filtration medium of much higher porosity. Such a medium is agarose gel.

II. AGAR AND AGAROSE

Agarose is a constituent of agar, the well-known polysaccharide from red algae. The porosity of agar gel has been utilized in scientific work ever since 1907 when Field and Teague (8) introduced this gel as

183

a support in electrophoresis experiments. Polson (9) was the first to suggest the use of granulated agar gel as a medium for gel filtration. This potential use has, however, been severely limited due to the poorly defined composition of commercially available agar and its gelling and adsorption properties which vary from batch to batch.

These unsatisfactory characteristics can, according to Araki (10), be ascribed to the fact that agar consists of two different polysaccharides, namely, agaropectin and agarose. Agaropectin, a typical pectic substance containing a high percentage of sulfate and carboxyl groups, imparts to the agar all the undesirable adsorption effects observed in agar gel electrophoresis and agar gel filtration. Agarose, on the other hand, is an unchanged polysaccharide which consists of alternating D-galactose and 3,6-anhydro-L-galactose units. It has at least the same good gelling properties as agar.

This discovery of Araki did not immediately lead to the replacement of agar by agarose in all scientific work. Araki's method of separating the two polysaccharides by acetylation and subsequent extraction with chloroform was somewhat too complicated and laborious for widespread use. The real breakthrough for agarose did not come until Hjertén (11) developed a simple technique to remove the agaropectin from agar solutions by precipitation with cetylpyridinium chloride.

III. AGAROSE GEL IN BEAD FORM

Soon afterward agarose became a worthy addition to the group of gel filtration media by the elegant work of Hjertén (12) and Bengtsson and Philipson (13). These investigators independently developed procedures for bead-gelling of agarose solutions. Bengtsson and Philipsson pressed an agarose or agar solution through a narrow orifice into a cold organic solvent, whereas Hjertén suspended agarose solutions in an organic solvent by using an appropriate emulsifier. Photomicrographs of agarose beads prepared according to the method of Hjertén are presented in Figure 1. The photograph to the right was obtained by the dark field technique, whereas the left picture was taken with illumination provided by a conventional condenser. Very hard film was used to increase the visibility of the granular structure. The nature of these "granules" within the beads is not quite well understood as yet. Their dimensions appear several orders of magnitude too large to reflect the porosity of the gel.

IV. THE DIFFERENCE BETWEEN BEADS AND GRANULES

The development of the bead-gelling procedures has been of great importance for two reasons:

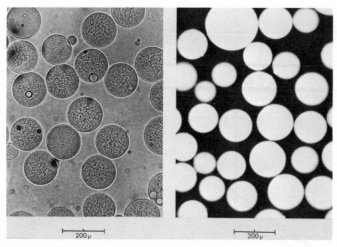

Fig. 1. Photomicrographs of Sepharose 4 B. The right-hand picture shows a dark-field preparation. The photograph to the left was obtained by conventional bright-field microscopy.

1. Because of their superior hydrodynamic properties the beaded gels are much easier to handle and greatly decrease the problem of compaction and clogging that one encounters when using granulated gel.

2. Beaded agarose gels have a greater separation power than granulated agarose gels. This amazing phenomenon is illustrated in Figure 2. Here the elution profiles of a number of specially prepared dextran fractions from columns packed with beads and granules are compared. The two gels were prepared from the same agarose batch, and they had the same agarose concentration and particle size. Comparison of the elution profiles and the K_{av} values shows that the exclusion limit of the granulated gel is higher and that its separation efficiency is lower than that of the beaded gel. These differences become even more manifest when the K_{av} values are plotted versus the $\overline{M}_W$ values on a logarithmic scale to obtain the so-called selectivity curves (lower part of Fig. 2). The beaded gel has a much steeper selectivity curve which clearly implies greater separation power.

So far this difference between beaded and granulated agarose gels is not very well understood. It has been suggested that during the bead-gelling process a "skin" of lower porosity is formed thus reducing the exclusion limit of the gel beads. However, this hypothesis appears not to be in agreement with the findings of Laurent, who has applied his theory on the Sephadex gel filtration mechanism (14) to agarose

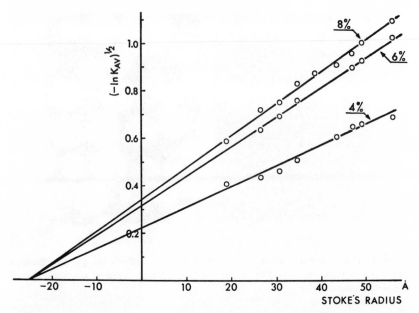

Fig. 2. Comparison of the separation characteristics of beaded and granulated agaros gels. The upper part of the figure shows the elution profiles of special dextran preparations of varied average molecular weights. In the lower part the concomitant selectivity curves are presented. The dextran preparations were submitted to gel filtration one by one, except for preparations 3 and 4, which were applied as a mixture. The numbers above the peaks represent the K_{av} values calculated from the elution volumes at the summits. The bed dimensions were identical for both gels: 1.5×25 cm. The flow rate was 5 ml/cm²-hr. (Adapted from author's unpublished work.)

gels. The theory of Laurent which presupposes that the gel matrix consists of a network of randomly but homogeneously distributed rodlike fibers, can be described by the equation:

$$(-\ln K_{av})^{\frac{1}{2}} = (\pi L)^{\frac{1}{2}} \, (^rS + r_R) \qquad (1)$$

where ^rS is the Stokes radius of the molecules subjected to gel filtration, r_R is the radius of the fibers, and L is the concentration of the fibers. Obviously, L and r_R are constants for a given gel and, consequently, a plot of $(-\ln K_{av})^{\frac{1}{2}}$ versus ^rS should result in a straight line. Laurent (15) did obtain this linear relationship for beaded agarose gels when plotting the data from gel filtration experiments with specially prepared Ficoll fractions of well-defined $\overline{M}_W$ (Fig. 3).

Since eq. (1) is theoretically based on a homogeneous distribution of the network fibers in a gel, Laurent's results appear to invalidate

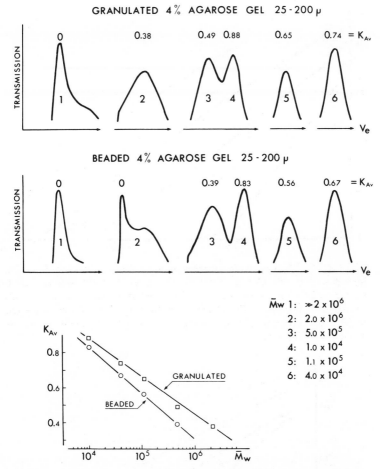

Fig. 3. A graphic validation of the gel filtration theory of Laurent as applied to beaded agarose gels of, respectively, 4, 6, and 8% concentration. The plotted Stokes radii and K_{av} values belong to special Ficoll preparations. (Adapted from Laurent (15).)

the hypothesis that the "skin" of agarose beads has a higher density of matrix material than the "inside." Neither is the "skin-hypothesis" supported by the shape of the selectivity curves (K_{av}–log M plots) obtained from agarose gel filtration experiments with proteins and specially prepared dextran fractions which are presented in Figures 4 and 5. The selectivity curves of a gel may be considered to reflect the size distribution of the "pores." A skin would make the gel pores above a certain limit inaccessible to those large solute molecules that other-

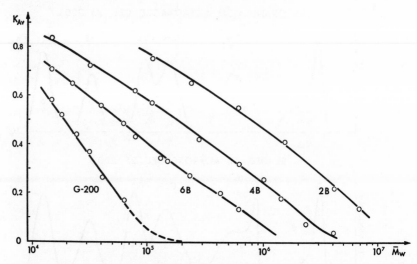

Fig. 4. Th dextran–molecular-weight selectivity curves of Sephadex G-200, Sepharose 6 B (ca. 6% agarose gel), Sepharose 4 B (ca. 4% agarose gel) and Sepharose 2 B (ca. 2% agarose gel). The dextran preparations used to obtain the plotted data were specially prepared fractions of very narrow molecular weight distribution. (Adapted from hitherto unpublished data kindly provided by Dr. K. Granath, Uppsala.)

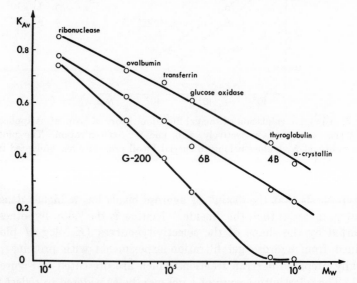

Fig. 5. The protein–molecular-weight selectivity curves of Sephadex G-200, Sepharose 6 B (experimental batch) and Sepharose 4 B. (Adapted from author's unpublished work.)

wise would have "fitted in," and would thus asymmetrically narrow the "apparent-pore-size" distribution. This would inevitably cause the selectivity curves to bend sharply. No such trend can, however, be observed in the curves of Figures 4 and 5. Thus, at present it is not clear why the porosities of beaded and granulated agarose gels are so different. In this connection it should be mentioned that great differences in porosity have been observed even between various gel batches of exactly the same agarose concentration. Apparently, there are, in addition to the agarose concentration, many other factors that influence the gel porosity. Most of these factors are still a matter of conjecture, but it appears quite certain that the temperature gradient during gelling and the molecular weight distribution of the agarose are of importance. An agarose gel can, therefore, never be characterized by its concentration alone.

V. SELECTIVITY CURVES

Molecular-weight selectivity curves, as in Figures 4 and 5, can be considered to characterize the gels quite adequately. However, this way of characterization is not absolutely correct, since the K_{av} values are a function of the molecular size rather than the molecular weight. This becomes quite obvious when one compares the curves in Figure 4 to those in Figure 5. The molecular-weight exclusion limits are about three times higher for the compact globular proteins than for the randomly coiled dextran chain molecules. In fact, the protein selectivity curve of Sepharose 6 B almost coincides with the dextran selectivity curve of Sepharose 4 B. A more unambiguous characterization can be achieved by plotting K_{av} versus the logarithm of the Stokes radius (^{r}S), or, in accordance with the Laurent theory, $(-\log K_{av})^{\frac{1}{2}}$ versus ^{r}S (cf. Fig. 3). However, accurate values of Stokes radii are not always readily available. Moreover, for conversion of Stokes radius to molecular weight, which is usually the quantity of greater interest, the sedimentation constant and the partial specific volume have to be known. Therefore, many investigators prefer the admittedly less correct but also much less complicated molecular-weight selectivity curves.

VI. FRACTIONATION OF PROTEINS

It is interesting to note that the selectivity curves of the various agarose gels slope to a lesser extent than the Sephadex G-200 curve (cf. Figs. 4 and 5). This indicates that the Sephadex gel has a superior separation power. Comparison of serum elution patterns very clearly brings out this difference. Figure 6 shows that serum can be fraction-

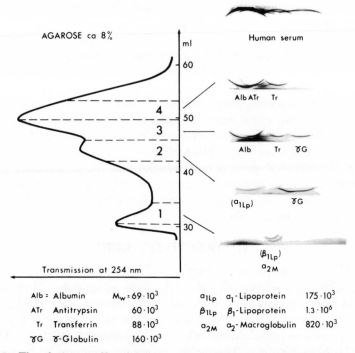

Fig. 6. The elution profile of human serum obtained by gel filtration on a beaded ca. 8% agarose gel (to the left) and the immunoelectropherograms of effluent fractions 1, 2, 3, and 4 (to the right). Bed dimensions: 1.5 × 50 cm. Eluant: 0.1M Tris–HCl/0.5M NaCl/pH 8.0. Flow rate: 2 ml/cm²-hr. The immunoelectropherograms were obtained in the conventional way except that agarose was used instead of agar. (Adapted from unpublished work by H. Lundgren and M. K. Joustra.)

ated on a ca. 8% agarose gel in a fashion reminiscent of the well-known serum separation achieved with Sephadex G-200. The immunoelectropherograms of the various fractions reveal, as could be expected, that the peaks contain consecutively macroglobulin, gamma globulin and albumin. By comparing the elution patterns of Figure 7 we learn, however, that the serum fractionation by Sephadex G-200 is considerably more efficient than those that can be accomplished by the various agarose gels.

Increasing the agarose concentration from ca. 6% does not seem to increase the separation power at all, as judged from the troughs between the gamma globulin and albumin peaks. The exclusion limit decreases, however, as is obvious from the increasing height of the "void volume" peaks. Thus it appears hardly worth while to utilize agarose gels for fractionation of proteins of molecular weights below

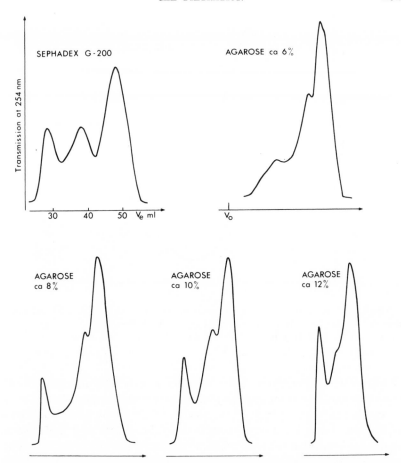

Fig. 7. Comparison of human serum elution profiles obtained by gel filtration on Sephadex G-200 and on beaded agarose gels of 6, 8, 10, and 12%, respectively. The various gel beds were almost equal in size (ca. 1.5 × 50 cm). Eluant: 0.1M Tris–HCl/0.5M NaCl/pH 8.0. Flow rate: 4 ml/cm²-hr. (Adapted from unpublished work by M. K. Joustra and H. Lundgren.)

300,000. However, since agarose gels are more rigid than Sephadex G-200 and consequently become compacted to a lesser degree, they may be used whenever a high flow rate is considered of more importance than a sharp separation. For fractionation of proteins of molecular weights above 300,000, Sepharose 6 B generally appears to be the gel of choice. In Figure 8 two representative examples of such protein fractionations are shown. The a-crystallin $(M = 10^6)$ had been prepared according to the method of van Dam and Ten Cate (16) whose most essential purification step consists of gel filtration on Sephadex

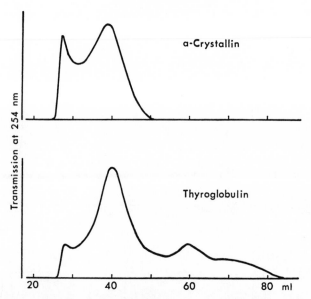

Fig. 8. The elution profiles of two protein preparations obtained by gel filtration on Sepharose 6 B (experimental batch). Bed dimensions: 1.5 × 50 cm. Eluant: $0.1M$ Tris–HCl/$0.5M$ NaCl/ph 8.0. Flow rate: 8 ml/cm²-hr. Samples: *1*. 1 ml α-crystallin solution (10 mg/ml); *2*. 1 ml thyroglobulin solution (15 mg/ml).

G-200. The thyroglobulin $(M = 650,000)$ was a "chromatographically pure" preparation from a well-known biochemical supply house.

Another interesting fractionation achieved on Sepharose 6 B is shown in Figures 9 and 10. Bovine colostrum (diluted 1:2 with buffer solution) was separated into nine distinct peaks on a bed of ca. $1m$ height. Disc-electrophoretic analysis of the peak fractions revealed, as of course could be expected, a separation of the colostrum proteins according to size. The first three peaks contained casein, whereas peaks 4 through 7 had as their major constituents: gamma globulin, serum-albumin, β-lactoglobulin, and α-lactalbumin, respectively. Peak 8 did not contain protein material and was not further identified. The content of peak 9 was found to be lactoflavin. In milk and colostrum about 90% of the casein is present as a calcium caseinate–phosphate complex (17). These casein micelles cover a wide range of "molecular weights," from about 10 million upward. One would, of course, expect these large micelles to be totally excluded from a gel like Sepharose 6 B. However, the casein micelles disintegrate rapidly when the concentration of the calcium ions in their microenvironment is decreased (17,18). During the gel filtration experiment depicted in Fig. 9

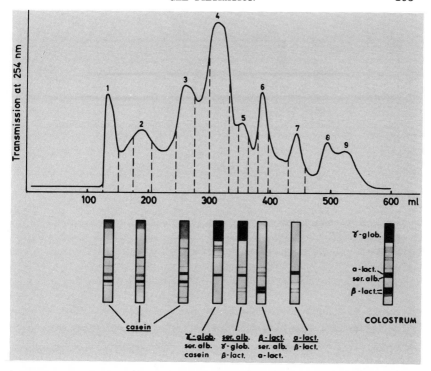

Fig. 9. The elution profile of bovine colostrum obtained by gel filtration on Sepharose 6 B (experimental batch). Bed dimensions: 2.5 × 94 cm. Eluant: 0.1M Tris-HCl/1.0M NaCl/pH 8.0. Sample: 5 ml bovine colostrum (diluted 1:2 with eluant). Flow rate: 1 ml/cm²-hr. The lower part of the figure shows the disc-electropherograms of peak fractions 1 through 7. The disc-electrophoresis experiments were conducted in the conventional way using polyacrylamid gel. (Adapted from unpublished work by H. Lundgren and M. K. Joustra.)

free calcium was, of course, continuously separated from the micelles, causing their desintegration. When CaCl₂ was added to the eluting buffer (Fig. 10) the major part of the casein was, as expected, eluted in the void volume. It remains, however, somewhat amazing that the casein micelles disintegrated into smaller units of distinct size ranges (Fig. 9; peaks 2 and 3) rather than into casein molecules (M = 24,000–122,000) which then would have been eluted in peaks 5 through 7.

VII. FRACTIONATION OF VIRUSES AND NUCLEIC ACIDS

Agarose gels of lower concentration than Sepharose 6 B (e.g., Sepharose 4 B and Sepharose 2 B) are too porous to be of great use in protein fractionation. Their applications lie mainly in the fields of

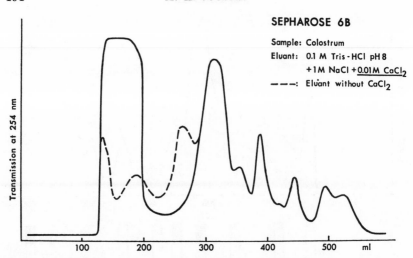

Fig. 10. Experimental conditions were the same as described for Fig. 9 except that the eluant was $0.1M$ in respect to $CaCl_2$.

virology and nucleic acid chemistry. In Figures 11–13 some typical application examples of these highly porous gels are presented. Figure 11 shows the separation of adeno- and poliovirus achieved on Sepharose 2 B. The adenovirus, which has an approximate size of 1000 Å, is eluted in the void volume, whereas the poliovirus (ca. 280

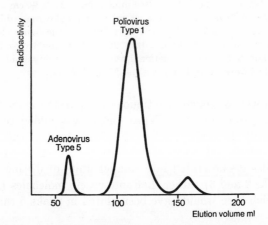

Fig. 11. Separation profile of a mixture of ^{32}P-labeled adenovirus and poliovirus obtained by gel filtration on Sepharose 2 B. Bed dimensions: 2.1×56 cm. Eluant: $0.002M$ sodium phosphate/$0.15M$ NaCl/pH 7.2. Flow rate: 2 ml/cm²-hr. (Adapted from unpublished data kindly provided by Drs. S. Bengtsson and L. Philipson, Uppsala.)

Å) has a K_{av} value of about 0.5. The third small peak is caused by free radioactive phosphate. Figure 12 shows the purification of satellite tobacco necrosis virus by gel filtration on Sepharose 4 B (19). This virus has a size of ca. 170 Å. Figure 13 shows a good example of the usefulness of Sepharose 2 B for the separation of nucleic acids. KB cells were infected with poliovirus. After the synthesis of KB-cell nucleic acids had been inhibited with actinomycin, radioactive phosphate was added. Since the synthesis of polio-RNA is not affected by the antibiotic, only this nucleic acid did become labeled with [32]P. The elution profile obtained by monitoring the radioactivity and the extinction at 260 nm reveals that the RNA of the virus can be separated from the nucleic acids of its host and that also the study of double- and single-stranded nucleic acids is made feasible by this technique.

VIII. GEL STRUCTURE

Finally, some remarks should be made about the relation between structure and porosity of agarose gels. In contrast to dextran the agarose is not caused to gel by the introduction of covalent crosslinkages. It is assumed that agarose molecules are held together in a gel structure by hydrogen bonding. Some doubt has, however, been cast on this hypothesis by the observation that agarose gels are not destroyed in $8M$ urea solutions. The porosity of agarose gels decreases, as we have seen, with an increase in concentration of matrix material. This is,

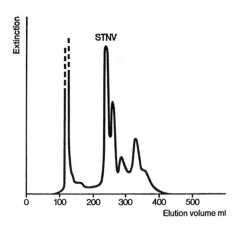

Fig. 12. Purification of satellite tobacco necrosis virus on Sepharose 4 B. Bed dimensions: 2×105 cm. Eluant: 0.05 sodium phosphate/$0.001M$ MgSO$_4$/pH 7.2. Sample: 4 ml of a solution obtained after redissolving the "$1.75M$ ammonium sulfate precipitate" from leaf extract. (Adapted from Fridborg et al. (19).)

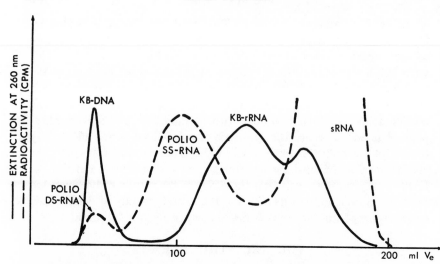

Fig. 13. Fractionation of nucleic acids on Sepharose 2 B. Bed dimensions: 2.1 × 51 cm. Eluant: 0.002M sodium phosphate/0.001M MgCl$_2$/pH 6.0. Sample: 2 ml of a nucleic acid preparation obtained from polio-infected KB-cells. The ^{32}P labeling took place after inhibition with actinomycin thus restricting the radioactive label to the polio-RNA. KB-DNA and KB-rRNA denote the nucleic acids from KB-cells. DS-RNA and SS-RNA denote double-stranded and single-stranded RNA, respectively. (Adapted from data kindly provided by Drs. B. Öberg and L. Philipson, Uppsala. A much more detailed description of these investigations has been submitted to the *Journal of Virology*.)

of course, also a well-known and well-understood characteristic of Sephadex gels. Therefore, it is striking that 6% agarose gel has a higher porosity than Sephadex G-200 (5% dextran gel). This curious phenomenon may, however, be tentatively understood by considering the simple model presented in Figure 14. Network B is obtained when

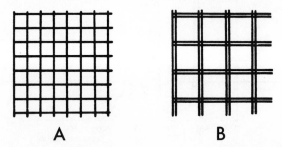

Fig. 14. A simple model for demonstration of the effect of "fiber thickness" on porosity. Network A and network B contain equal numbers of threads (fibers). Combining the threads, two by two, into thicker units, as in B, causes an enlargement of the mesh openings (pores).

the threads of network A are, two by two, combined into thicker units. It is obvious that by this manipulation the mesh openings (pores) have become larger whereas the number of threads (concentration of matrix material) has not been changed. This very simple model indicates that the difference in porosity between Sephadex and agarose gels may, at least partly, be understood in terms of fiber thickness. Support for this hypothesis has been provided by Laurent who has used eq. (1) to estimate the radii of the "rods" in agarose and Sephadex gels. From eq. (1) it is clear that when $(-\ln K_{av})^{\frac{1}{2}}$ is plotted versus r_s, the distance on the abcissa from origin to intersection is equal to r_R. From Figure 3 it can be seen that the fiber radius of agarose gels can be estimated to 25 Å. In a similar way Laurent arrived at a value of 7 Å for Sephadex gels. It appears that these values are in good harmony with the observed differences in porosity.

Summary

Agarose gels can be prepared in a range of porosity types which extends to far above that of Sephadex gels. In the range of comparable porosity types; however, Sephadex gels possess better separation qualities. The higher porosity of agarose gels may be attributed to "thicker fibers."

Beaded agarose gels have lower exclusion limits and higher separation power than granulated agarose gels. This phenomenon cannot be explained by a "skin effect." The gel filtration characteristics of an agarose gel are not determined by the agarose concentration alone. Such a gel is, however, adequately characterized by a so-called selectivity curve.

The protein and dextran molecular weight selectivity curves of some agarose gels are presented and discussed. The field of application of agarose gels is illustrated by some typical examples from the fields of protein chemistry, nucleic acid chemistry, and virology.

References

1. H. Determann, *Gelchromatographie,* Springer, Berlin, 1967.
2. B. Gelotte and J. Porath, in *Chromatography,* E. Heftmann, Ed., Reinhold, New York, 1967, p. 343.
3. M. K. Joustra, *Protides Biol. Fluids,* **14,** 533.
4. B. Gelotte, in *New Biochemical Separations,* A. T. James and E. T. Morris, Eds., Van Nostrand, Princeton, N. J., 1964, p. 93.
5. K. Granath, in *New Biochemical Separations,* A. T. James and E. T. Morris, Eds., Van Nostrand, Princeton, N. J., 1964, p. 111.
6. S. Hjertén and R. Mosbach, *Anal. Biochem.,* **3,** 109 (1962).

7. D. J. Lea and A. H. Sehon, *Can. J. Chem.*, **40**, 159 (1962).
8. C. W. Field and O. Teague, *J. Exptl. Med.*, **9**, 86 (1907).
9. A. Polson, *Biochim. Biophys. Acta*, **50**, 565 (1961).
10. C. Araki, *Bull. Chem. Soc. Japan*, **29**, 543 (1956).
11. S. Hjertén, *Biochim. Biophys. Acta*, **62**, 445 (1962).
12. S. Hjertén, *Biochim. Biophys. Acta*, **79**, 393 (1964).
13. S. Bengtsson and L. Philipson, *Biochim. Biophys. Acta*, **79**, 399 (1964).
14. T. C. Laurent and J. Killander, *J. Chromatog.*, **14**, 317 (1964).
15. T. C. Laurent, *Biochim. Biophys. Acta*, **136**, 199 (1967).
16. A. F. van Dam and G. Ten Cate, *Biochim. Biophys. Acta*, **121**, 183 (1966).
17. P. H. von Hippel and D. F. Waugh, *J. Am. Chem. Soc.*, **77**, 4311 (1955).
18. H. Nitschman, *Helv. Chim. Acta*, **32**, 1258 (1949).
19. K. Fridborg, S. Hjertén, S. Höglund, A. Liljas, B. K. S. Lundberg, P. Oxelfelt, L. Philipson, and B. Strandberg, *Proc. Natl. Acad. Sci. U.S.*, **54**, 513 (1965).

On the Theoretical Aspects of Gel Chromatography *

Torvard C. Laurent, Björn Öbrink, Krister Hellsing, and
Åke Wasteson

*Department of Medical Chemistry, University of Uppsala,
Uppsala, Sweden*

The name gel chromatography will be used in this chapter for the process in which substances are chromatographed on gels and separated according to size rather than chemical composition. A large number of uncharged gels have been used for gel chromatography, e.g., crosslinked dextran, agarose, and polyacrylamide. Even on these gels, however, specific adsorption of a solute to the gel matrix can occur. It is known that aromatic compounds are adsorbed to dextran gels (1). These adsorption phenomena will be disregarded in the following. Gel chromatography has also been referred to as gel filtration

* Supported by grants from the Swedish Medical Research Council (B68–13X–4–04C, K67–13X–2228–01), the Swedish Cancer Society, Knut och Alice Wallenbergs stiftelse, Konung Gustaf V:s 80-årsfond, Pharmacia AB and the University of Uppsala. This is No. 17 in the series *Interaction between Polysaccharides and Other Macromolecules*.

(2), exclusion chromatography (3), molecular sieve chromatography (4), and gel permeation chromatography (5). As all these terms imply that the basic mechanism of the chromatographic process is known and as some of them give an incorrect impression of the process, we prefer to use the simple name gel chromatography (6).

The history of the development of gel chromatography has recently been presented in an excellent review by Determann (7). It was not until Porath and Flodin (2) started to use crosslinked dextran, that the technique was commonly used, and it has now become one of the most important tools in biochemical research. Our intention is not to review this versatile technique, as a number of good reviews have already been written (7–10) but to discuss some of the theoretical aspects of the process, which leads to a molecular size fractionation, as well as some practical consequences of the theories.

I. DISCUSSION OF THE BASIC MECHANISM

In all the theories hitherto formulated, it is assumed that the gel column consists of a stationary gel phase and a mobile liquid phase and that the solute molecules are partitioned between the two phases during the chromatographic process. The partition of large molecules in favor of the liquid phase leading to a molecular size fractionation, has been explained in the following ways:

The Exclusion Theory. Due to the steric configuration of the gel matrix the chromatographed solute is excluded from a certain part of the gel volume. The excluded part increases with increasing molecular size of the solute.

The Theory of Restricted Diffusion. Frictional effects in the gel matrix leads to a decrease in the diffusion rate of the solute and thus equilibration between the gel phase and the buffer phase during the chromatographic experiment is not attained. The frictional effects will increase with increasing molecular size of the solute.

Partition Due to Molecular Surface Forces. The partition between the gel and the buffer phases is determined by chemical interaction between the solute molecule and the gel matrix. As the interacting forces are a function of the surface area of the solute molecule, they will increase with increasing molecular size.

Partition Due to the Osmotic Pressure in the Gel. The high osmotic pressure in the gel will increase the chemical potential of the solute and this increase is a function of its molar volume and thus its molecular size. The increase in chemical potential will lead to an unequal partition between the gel phase and the buffer phase.

A. The Exclusion Theory

As early as 1956, Lathe and Ruthven interpreted the results of chromatographic experiments on a starch column in terms of steric exclusion of solute molecules from the starch granules (11). This concept has since been developed by a number of authors (3,12–18). Several of them have assumed that the gel has a given structure and have tried to correlate the exclusion of various molecules from such a structure with the experimental data.

Porath (13) assumed that the spaces in the gel were conical and Squire (16) extended the hypothesis to include cones, cylinders, and crevices. Both treatments lead, however, to equations containing constants, which are difficult to correlate to the gel concentration. It is therefore not possible to rigorously test the validity of the equations. Agneray (17) assigned a cubical network structure to the gel. Laurent and Killander (15) had earlier, however, treated the gel matrix as a three-dimensional network of randomly distributed fibers, which is a much more attractive model (Fig. 1). Using an equation proposed by Ogston (19), they calculated the exclusion of spherical particles of known sizes from the fiber network assuming given values for the radius and the concentration of the fiber. As the treatment developed by Laurent and Killander relating the structure of a gel to its exclusion properties seems to be the most realistic so far, it will be discussed in detail.

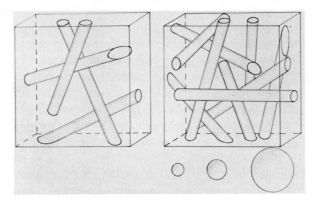

Fig. 1. Representation of the structure, which Laurent and Killander (15) assigned to the gel matrix. The exclusion of spherical particles of different sizes is determined by the spaces between the fibers. The available space is, provided that the fibers are uniformly thick, a function of the concentration of the fibers and the radius of the sphere. The picture illustrates two gels of different concentrations and three different sized spheres.

Hohn and Pollman (14) and Ackers (18) have disregarded the structure of the gel and assumed that the sizes of the free spaces in the gel
follow a Boltzmann (14) or a Gaussian distribution (17). Experimental data are in accordance with these assumptions. The statistical
distribution of the space sizes is, however, already a feature of
Laurent and Killander's treatment. Further the "nonstructural"
approach does not provide any structural information on the gel
matrix and the influence of the concentration of gel material on the
exclusion properties cannot be predicted.

As mentioned before, Ogston (19) has calculated the fraction of
the total space in which a spherical particle can be placed in a
network of infinitely long randomly distributed rigid rods and his
equation using the symbols defined by Laurent and Killander (15)
may be written

$$K_{av} = \exp[-\pi L (r_r + r_s)^2] \tag{1}$$

where K_{av} is the fraction of the total space available for a spherical
molecule with the radius r_s, L is the concentration of fiber expressed
in cm/cm^3, and r_r is the radius of the cylindrical fiber.

Siegel and Monty (20) have later pointed out that a convenient way
of writing the equation is:

$$(-\ln K_{av})^{0.5} = (\pi L)^{0.5} (r_r + r_s) \tag{2}$$

In testing the validity of the equation for an unknown system, a plot
of $(-\ln K_{av})^{0.5}$ versus r_s should give a straight line providing the
system can be regarded as a three-dimensional fibrous network. The
intercept on the r_s axis should be equal to the negative fiber radius.
The slope of the line can be used to calculate L and the intercept on
the ordinate is equal to $(\pi L r_r^2)^{0.5}$ which is the square root of the volume
fraction occupied by the fibers in the system.

In their original test of the above hypothesis, Laurent and Killander
(15) used experimental data obtained on *dextran gels* (Sephadex gels).
They assumed that the fiber radius of the dextran chain was 7 Å and
showed that the partition coefficient of solutes with very different
Stokes radii followed eq. (1) if an appropriate value of L was assigned
to each gel. The data they used have been replotted according to
eq. (2) (Fig. 2a) and the lines have been drawn on the assumption
that the fiber radius is 7 Å. The slope of the lines is proportional
to the square root of the dextran concentration (Fig. 2b) as expected
because L in eqs. (1) and (2) is a concentration parameter. From
Figure 2b, it can be deduced that 1 g of dextran is equivalent to
3.8×10^{13} cm of fiber. This corresponds only to about 20% of the length

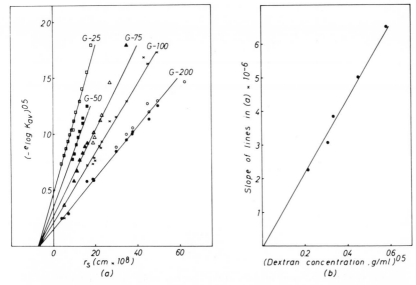

Fig. 2. (*a*) The data used by Laurent and Killander (15) from chromatographic studies on dextran gels have been replotted according to eq. (2) and the full lines have been drawn on the assumption that the fiber radius is 7 Å. According to the theory, the slope of the lines should be proportional to the square root of the dextran concentrations in the gel grains and this is verified in (*b*).

of a fully stretched polysaccharide chain and it must therefore be assumed that the chain is coiled. There is at present no other experimental verification for this degree of coiling.

The second gel to be tested was a crosslinked *hyaluronic acid* (21). A replot of the data is given in Figure 3. The full line corresponds to that expected theoretically for an extended polysaccharide chain with a disaccharide unit of length 10.3 Å. Electron microscopic studies on hyaluronic acid by Fessler and Fessler indicate that hyaluronic acid has this configuration (22). Gel chromatographic and electron microscopic data are thus in very good agreement.

Data from *agarose gels* (23) when plotted according to eq. (2) gave a fiber radius of approximately 25 Å (Fig. 4). Thus, 1 g of agarose was equivalent to approximately 7×10^{12} cm fiber. From the concentrations of the gels and the volume fractions occupied by the fibers, it was concluded that the fibers must contain 35–50% water. Light scattering was performed to verify these fiber parameters (24). However, these measurements could only be performed at much lower concentrations of agarose than those existing in the gels. The scattering data were evaluated as described by Casassa (25) and a typical

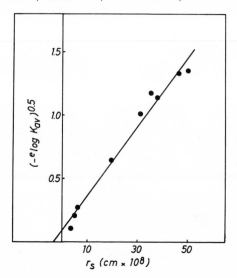

Fig. 3. Gel chromatographic data obtained on a 1.45% hyaluronic acid gel (21) plotted according to eq. (2). The line is identical with that predicted by theory assuming hyaluronic acid is an extended linear polysaccharide chain with a disaccharide unit length of 10.3 Å and a radius of 3.5 Å.

result is shown in Figure 5. From the slope of the line in Figure 5 and similar experiments, one can calculate that the mass/length ratio of the agarose fibers is in the range of 1.2×10^{-13} to 2.1×10^{-13} g/cm. The corresponding values calculated from the gel chromatographic experiments were 1.2×10^{-13} to 1.7×10^{-13} g/cm and are thus in very good agreement.

Fawcett and Morris (26) have made an extensive study of *polyacrylamide gels* varying two parameters, i.e., the total concentration of gel material and the percentage of crosslinker in the gel. When the various gels were studied in gel chromatography, the results were in good agreement with eq. (1). For a specified concentration of crosslinker, L was always directly proportional to the concentration of gel material. The fiber radius varied with the percentage of crosslinker used; the more crosslinker the thicker the fiber.

Partridge (27) has recently performed gel chromatographic experiments on an *elastin gel*. The data is in accordance with eq. (2) and gives a fiber radius of 8 Å.

The equation deduced by Ogston (eq. (1)) is valid for excluded spherical particles. In all the experimental work reviewed above, solute molecules have been regarded as spherical with radii equal to the

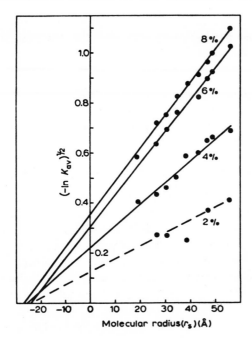

Fig. 4. Data from the chromatography of Ficoll fractions on agarose gels of 2, 4, 6 and 8% concentration, plotted according to eq. (2). (Taken from Laurent, *Biochim. Biophys. Acta,* **136,** 199 (1967)).

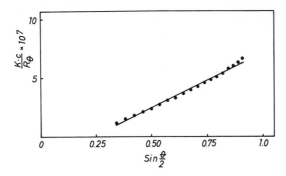

Fig. 5. Plot according to Casassa (25) of light-scattering data obtained on 0.09% agarose. The symbols are defined in Casassa's paper. From the slope of the line one can calculate a mass/length ratio of 2.1×10^{-13} g/cm. (See also Öbrink (24).)

Stokes radii as calculated from the diffusion constants of the compounds. Fischer (9) has pointed out that the treatment should also be valid for nonspherical molecules. If $r_s \gg r_r$, eq. (1) can be written

$$K_{av} = \exp\left(-\frac{LA}{4}\right) \qquad (3)$$

where A is the surface area of the globular molecule. According to Fischer, any molecule with a positively curved surface can be accommodated in eq. (3).

B. The Theory of Restricted Diffusion

Ackers (28), studying various proteins found a surprising difference between the partition coefficients obtained in chromatographic experiments and in equilibrium experiments with the dextran gel Sephadex G-200. This discrepancy was not found in experiments with the more concentrated gels Sephadex G-75 and G-100. In order to explain the results, he proposed that frictional effects in the Sephadex G-200 grains prevented equilibration during the chromatographic runs. The decrease in diffusion rates of large molecules in polysaccharide media is well known. Using an equation proposed by Renkin (29), he derived a parameter describing the restriction of the diffusion of a sphere through a membrane containing cylindrical pores in terms of the pore radius and sphere radius. This parameter was shown experimentally to be related to the partition coefficient obtained in gel chromatography provided the appropriate pore radius was selected for each gel. There are, however, strong arguments against such a hypothesis. If the gel chromatographic effect were due to local nonequilibria, there should be a pronounced dependence of the elution volumes on flow rate and grain size in the column. This is rarely observed.

It has not been possible in our laboratory to repeat the experiments described by Ackers, on which he based his hypothesis. We obtain the same partition coefficients in chromatographic experiments and batch experiments with Sephadex G-200. One batch experiment is depicted in Figure 6.

C. Partition Due to Molecular Surface Forces

Brønsted (30) has pointed out that when a solute is partitioned between two phases, the partition coefficient (K) can be described by a Boltzmann distribution in which for a large compact molecule like a protein, its surface area (A) is one of the parameters:

$$K = \exp[-A\lambda/kT] \qquad (4)$$

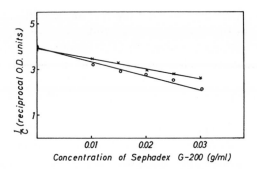

Fig. 6. Determination of the partition coefficients for human serum albumin ($\times$) and human IgG (O) partitioned between Sephadex G-200 and buffer in batch experiments. The proteins used were homogeneous substances which in the final steps of purification were chromatographed on Sephadex G-200. Various amounts of dry Sephadex G-200 were weighed into two series of volumetric flasks. To each series was added a constant volume of an albumin or IgG solution, respectively. The dextran gel was allowed to swell for 48 hr and the volume in each flask was made up to 10 ml. The gel grains were allowed to settle and the optical density at 280 mμ was recorded after suitable dilution (4 and 10 times, respectively) of the supernatant. The reciprocal of this value has been plotted in the figure versus the amount of dry Sephadex/ml. The partition coefficient is calculated from the equation

$$K_{av} = 1 + (1/k) \cdot (\text{slope/intercept on ordinate})$$

where k is the volume occupied by 1 g of swollen dextran gel (in this experiment 19.3 ml). K_{av} obtained for serum albumin is 0.435 and for IgG 0.19 in close agreement with values from gel chromatography (15).

λ is a parameter determined by the nature of the surface forces between the solute and the two phases, k is Boltzmann's constant and T the absolute temperature.

Albertsson (31) has used this concept to explain unequal partition of macromolecules between two polymer phases. He found in some of his experiments that the molecules were partitioned approximately according to their surface areas.

If eqs. (3) and (4) are compared, one can see that the exclusion hypothesis and the surface forces hypothesis lead to very similar mathematical expressions and that the main difference is the absolute temperature parameter. Theoretically, it should therefore be possible to differentiate between them by measuring the temperature dependence during gel chromatography.

There are a few reports on the temperature dependence. Moore and Hendrickson (32) chromatographed standard compounds on a polystyrene gel in three different solvents and at three different temperatures (55, 90, and 125°) and did not find any significant difference in the results from the various runs. Öbrink and co-workers (33) chromatographed well-characterized Ficoll fractions on a Sephadex G-200 column at 9 and 60°. They observed small increases in the partition coefficients with increasing temperature but these were only a third of those predicted from eq. (4). Shrinking of the gel was observed during the experiments and the effects on the partition coefficients could best be explained by a change in the gel structure. The data indicated that the shrinking was due to an increased coiling of the dextran chains so that the dextran fibers became shorter and thicker. When a plot was made according to eq. (2), the radii of the dextran chain at 9° and 60° were found to be 6 Å and 8 Å respectively. According to eq. ·(4), such a plot should pass through the origin but this was definitely not the case. The increased coiling at higher temperature was verified by fluorescence polarization measurements. Although the experiments were not ideal for differentiating between the two hypothetical explanations for gel chromatography, they favored the exclusion hypothesis. The shrinkage of dextran gels with increasing temperature has also been observed by other authors (34).

A considerable temperature dependence has been observed during chromatography on gels in some instances, where, for other reasons, an exclusion effect is not present (35).

D. Partition Due to the Osmotic Pressure in the Gel

A high osmotic pressure in the gel will influence the chemical potential of a compound present in the gel. This treatment has been applied to partitioning in ion exchange chromatography, where very high swelling pressures have been estimated for the resin granules. Ginzburg and Cohen (36) have concluded that the size fractionation ,in gel chromatography is essentially due to an osmotic effect.

The relationship between the partition coefficient, the activity coefficient and the osmotic pressure in the gel given by Ogston (37, eq. 18) may be written in a modified form:

$$\ln \frac{\gamma'}{\gamma''} = \ln \left[\frac{C''}{C'} \right] - \frac{\pi v}{RT} \tag{5}$$

where γ' and C' are the activity coefficient and equilibrium concentration of the solute in the buffer phase and γ'' and C'' those of the solute in the gel phase. π is the osmotic pressure in the gel and v the molar volume of the solute. C''/C' is equal to the partition coefficient, represented by K_{av} elsewhere in this paper.

The osmotic pressures in dextran gels are not known. However, the osmotic pressures of dextran solutions of the same polymer concentrations should give a good approximation assuming the molecular weight of the polymer to be infinitely large. We have therefore used Hint's equation (38) to calculate the osmotic term in eq. (5) and Figure 7 demonstrates the influence of osmotic pressure on the partition between a buffer phase and two dextran gels, Sephadex G-200 and G-75. The osmotic effect seems to be of little practical importance in this system. The osmotic pressure in the hyaluronic acid gel described by Laurent (21) and discussed above may be obtained by extrapolation of data given by Laurent and Ogston (39). In this case, the osmotic effect has a negligible influence on the partition coefficient and will only affect the third decimal place. The osmotic pressures of the agarose gels are not known but are presumably lower than those of the dextran gels.

In summary, one can conclude that the evidence is strongly in favor of the theory that size fractionation in gel chromatography is due to an exclusion mechanism, even if other mechanisms may contribute to a

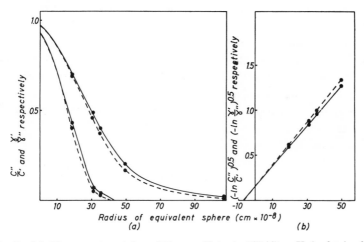

Fig. 7. (a) The experimental partition coefficients ($C''/C' = K_{av}$) obtained for ribonuclease, hemoglobin, serum albumin, and IgG in experiments with Sephadex G-200 and G-75 have been plotted versus their molecular radii (———). The ratio of the activity coefficients of the compounds in the liquid and gel compartments (γ'/γ'') have been calculated according to eq. (5) and plotted similarly (— — —). The difference between the two curves gives the contribution from the osmotic effect. It is approximately the same for all the dextran gels. (b) The effect is also demonstrated by plotting the data from Sephadex G-200 according to eq. (2). The parameters r_r and L obtained from the two lines differ by 10–15%.

lesser extent. There is an increasing amount of experimental support for the gel structure model, proposed by Laurent and Killander, and which was the basis for their theoretical calculations on the exclusion properties of various gels.

II. RESOLUTION IN GEL CHROMATOGRAPHY

For practical chromatographic work it is important to know in what molecular size range a certain gel has its greatest resolving power. The resolution between two compounds in a chromatogram is determined by the distance between their elution peaks (or difference in K_{av}) and the width of the peaks. If we disregard the increased zone width which is observed with increasing elution volume, we can obtain a measure of the resolving power in terms of changes of K_{av} with molecular size.

The resolution may then be defined as $-dK_{av}/dr_s$ and is obtained from eq. (1), which differentiated gives:*

$$-\frac{dK_{av}}{dr_s} = 2\pi L \,(r_s+r_r)\exp[\,-\pi L\,(r_s+r_r)^2] \qquad (6)$$

This function has a maximum value for $r_s+r_r=1/(2\pi L)^{\frac{1}{2}}$ or $K_{av}=$ 0.6065.

The resolutions obtained on chromatography with different dextran gels (Sephadex G-200, G-100, G-50 and G-25) and agarose gels (1, 2, and 4%) are shown in Figures 8 and 9. The values for L and r_r used in the calculations have been discussed above.

The more concentrated a gel is, the higher its resolving power. The molecular size range, where the gel will be useful is, however, narrow and appears at low molecular size values. If two gels with different fiber parameters, for example dextran and agarose gels, are compared, one finds that an increased fiber radius increases the range of usefulness of the gel and also shifts it to higher values. The resolving power is, however, drastically decreased.

As discussed above, no account has been taken during the calculations of the effect of zone spreading on the resolutions. The zone width increases with K_{av} and thus also with decreasing molecular size of the chromatographed substance (40,41). This means that the highest resolution is actually obtained at larger r_s values than are demonstrated in Figures 8 and 9.

---

* Dr. L. Fischer has kindly pointed out that for certain purposes, it is more appropriate to calculate $- dK_{av}/d \log r_s$.

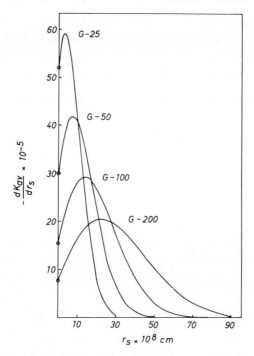

Fig. 8. The chromatographic resolution obtained on various dextran gels calculated as a function of the molecular radius for the substances chromatographed. No correction has been made for zone spreading.

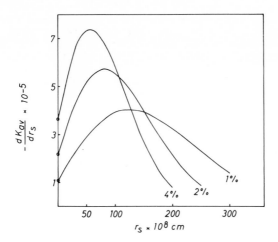

Fig. 9. The chromatographic resolution on agarose gels of various concentrations.

III. COMPARISON OF THE EXCLUSION IN POLYMER GELS AND POLYMER SOLUTIONS

The exclusion of a compound from a polymer gel can also be regarded as an increase in its activity coefficient in the presence of the polymer if the small osmotic pressure effect is disregarded. It should be possible to measure this increase not only in a polymer gel but also in polymer solutions.

There are a number of techniques, which have been used to determine the activity of proteins in polymer solutions. A discussion of the problem can be found in reference 42. A list of the investigations is given in Table I. The two polymers which have been most extensively studied are hyaluronic acid and dextran. The results indicate that the increase in activity of a compound in a polymer solution is very nearly the same, at least for moderately concentrated systems, as that registered in a gel of the same polymer at the same concentration provided that the soluble polymer has a sufficiently high molecular weight (42). The crosslinks in the gel thus do not influence the exclusion phenomenon—the important parameter is the concentration of polymer in the gel.

The work of Hellsing (49,50) warrants some comments in this connection. He added soluble polymers to the mobile phase during gel

TABLE I

Studies on the Exclusion of Proteins and Other Macromolecules
from Polymer Solutions

Author	Technique used	Polymer studied	Reference
Blumberg and Ogston (1956)	Sedimentation	Hyaluronic acid	(43)
Ogston and Phelps (1961)	Equilibrium dialysis	Hyaluronic acid	(44)
Laurent (1963)	Solubility studies	Dextran	(45,46)
Laurent and Ogston (1963)	Osmometry	Hyaluronic acid	(39)
Laurent (1964)	Equilibrium dialysis	Hyaluronic acid	(21)
Gerber and Schubert (1964)	Equilibrium dialysis	Chondroitin sulfate–protein complex	(47)
Preston et al. (1965)	Osmometry	Hyaluronic acid	(48)
Hellsing (1965, 1968)	Gel chromatography	Dextran, etc.	(49,50)
Ogston and Preston (1966)	Light scattering	Hyaluronic acid	(51)
Dudman (1966)	Solubility studies	Agar, gelatin, etc.	(52,53)

chromatography and as a result of the exclusion properties of the poly-mer, he observed a change in the partition between the gel phase and the mobile phase of albumin. This is shown in Figure 10. From the change in partition coefficient he could calculate the exclusion prop-erties of the soluble polymer and verify that soluble dextran has iden-tical effects on the activity coefficient of albumin as a dextran gel with the same concentration. The method used by Hellsing affords a very convenient way of studying exclusion properties of soluble polymers.

IV. USE OF GEL CHROMATOGRAPHY FOR ANALYTICAL PURPOSES

So far, the overwhelming use of gel chromatography has been for preparative work. The theoretical ground work has, however, provided a foundation for its use in analytical work too. It has been used for the following analyses.

A. Determination of Molecular Size

Regardless of which theoretical explanation is given for the gel chromatographic process (see above), the fractionation of compounds should depend on a size parameter (molecular radius, molar volume, molar surface area). It should thus be possible to determine a size parameter by gel chromatography. *There is, however, no theoretical justification for using gel chromatography to determine molecular weight a priori*, as is commonly believed. Only in the case of a series of homologous compounds, can one find a relationship between molecu-lar weight and molecular size. In this case, a gel column can be cali-

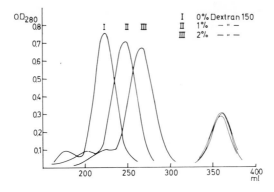

Fig. 10. Chromatography of serum albumin on a column of Sephadex G-200 in the absence of soluble dextran and with 1 and 2% dextran present in the mobile phase. (Taken from Hellsing, *Acta Chem. Scand.*, **19**, 1791 (1965).)

brated with standard compounds of known molecular weights. In all other instances, molecular weight determinations by gel chromatography alone are theoretically impossible.

The best examples of how gel chromatography can be used for analytical purposes are found in polymer chemistry. Moore and co-workers (5,32) have developed techniques for determining the molecular weight and the molecular weight dispersion of lipophilic polymers, for which well-characterized calibration fractions are available and this is now a commonly used technique. Granath and Kvist (54) have used the technique for distribution analysis of dextran fractions. Wasteson (55) has similarly developed the method for chondroitin sulfate. Figure 11 demonstrates the importance of having calibration fractions homologous to the unknown material to be studied. The molecular weight as a function of the partition coefficient on a gel column varies considerably between compounds. A very convenient way of preparing homogeneous calibration fractions for the determination is to fractionate a polydisperse polymer by gel chromatography on a preparative scale and determine the molecular weights of the subfractions by conventional methods (56).

The most common group of compounds, whose molecular weights have been determined by such methods are the proteins. A number

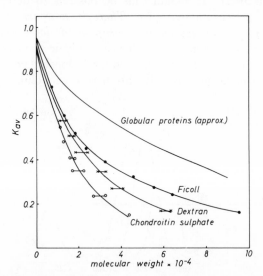

Fig. 11. The partition coefficients (K_{av}) between Sephadex G–200 and buffer have been measured for various series of homologous compounds (globular proteins, Ficoll-, dextran, and chondroitin sulfate fractions) and plotted against the molecular weight of the compounds.

of authors have obtained empirical relationships between molecular weight and elution volume in gel chromatography (57–61). The main reason why it has met with success is that most analyzed proteins are globular, resembling spherical molecules. The method breaks down immediately the protein has another shape, e.g., when it is denatured (20,62). The technique is thus very unreliable. A more reliable modification is probably that, in which the chains are denatured in guanidinium hydrochloride and the disulfide bonds are cleaved by reduction. The peptide chains will then all assume a random coil configuration (63). Even in this case, however, variations in amino acid composition can lead to different degrees of expansion of the coil. The technique also implies that there is only one peptide chain in the molecule.

In a recent communication, Grubisic et al. (64) proposed a universal relationship between the product of molecular weight and intrinsic viscosity for a polymer and its elution volume in gel chromatography. It was shown to be correct for a number of lipophilic polymers in organic solvents.

B. Determination of Diffusion Constants

In the treatment developed by Laurent and Killander discussed above, a relationship between the molecular radius and the partition coefficient in gel chromatography was derived. In testing the theory they used the Stokes radius for various substances. For any given molecule, this is the radius that a spherical molecule with the same diffusion constant would have. One should therefore be able to obtain approximate values for the diffusion constants of various compounds. Siegel and Monty (20) combined the diffusion constants obtained by gel chromatography with sedimentation data to obtain molecular weights of proteins. In later studies, Laurent and Granath (56) determined diffusion constants for dextran fractions in this way, which were in fair agreement with those obtained by other techniques. Wasteson has likewise studied chondroitin sulfate fractions (55).

It is too early to predict whether this way of estimating diffusion constants could become a generally acceptable technique.

C. Determination of Gel Structures and Polymer Parameters

The correlation between gel structures and their exclusion properties established by Laurent and co-workers (15,21,23) indicates that one should be able to determine fiber parameters such as length, thickness, and hydration by gel chromatography. One such attempt was made by Partridge on elastin gels (27). Other biological gels should be worth studying by this technique and some work along these lines is at present in progress in our laboratory.

Since polymer solutions exhibit the same exclusion properties as gels, it should be possible to derive, similar polymer parameters for the two systems. Hellsing's studies (49,50) on gel chromatography using polymers in the mobile phase, should be especially valuable for investigating soluble polymers.

D. Studies of Reacting Systems

If two compounds interact in a transport system, they will mutually affect their normal transport behavior. This effect may be studied in the ultracentrifuge, by electrophoresis and by chromatography. An excellent review on the phenomena has been written by Nichol et al. (65). Interaction during transport has also recently been described in gel chromatography (66–68) and the mathematical treatment has been modified for this special transport system (69). A discussion of the work is, however, outside the scope of this chapter.

V. SUMMARY

A review is given of the various explanations which have been proposed to account for the fractionation of molecules according to size by gel chromatography. Experimental evidence strongly favors the theory that the molecules are sterically excluded from the gel phase, and that this is the main mechanism. The theoretical treatment of the mechanism forms a basis for the use of gel chromatography as an analytical tool.

References

1. J. Porath, *Biochim. Biophys. Acta,* **39,** 193 (1960).
2. J. Porath and P. Flodin, *Nature,* **183,** 1657 (1959).
3. K. O. Pedersen, *Arch. Biochem. Biophys. Suppl.* **1,** 157 (1962).
4. S. Hjertén and R. Mosbach, *Anal. Biochem.,* **3,** 109 (1962).
5. J. C. Moore, *J. Polymer Sci. A,* **2,** 835 (1964).
6. H. Determann, *Angew. Chem.,* **76,** 635 (1964).
7. H. Determann, *Gelchromatographie,* Springer, Berlin, 1967.
8. B. Gelotte and J. Porath, "Gel Filtration," in *Chromatography,* 2 ed., E. Heftmann, Ed., Reinhold, New York, 1967, p. 343
9. L. Fischer, *Introduction to Gel Chromatography,* North-Holland Pub., Amsterdam, 1968.
10. P. Andrews, "Molecular Sieve Chromatography," *Brit. Med. Bull.,* **22,** 109 (1966).
11. G. H. Lathe and C. R. J. Ruthven, *Biochem. J.,* **62,** 665 (1956).

12. P. Flodin, "Dextran Gels and Their Applications in Gel Filtration." Dissertation, Uppsala, 1962.
13. J. Porath, *Pure Appl. Chem.*, **6**, 233 (1963).
14. Th. Hohn and W. Pollman, *Z. Naturforsch.*, **18b**, 919 (1963).
15. T. C. Laurent and J. Killander, *J. Chromatog.*, **14**, 317 (1964).
16. P. G. Squire, *Arch. Biochem. Biophys.*, **107**, 471 (1964).
17. J. Agneray, Doctoral Dissertation, University of Lille, 1965.
18. G. K. Ackers, *J. Biol. Chem.*, **242**, 3237 (1967).
19. A. G. Ogston, *Trans. Faraday Soc.*, **54**, 1754 (1958).
20. L. M. Siegel and K. J. Monty, *Biochim. Biophys. Acta*, **112**, 346 (1966).
21. T. C. Laurent, *Biochem. J.*, **93**, 106 (1964).
22. J. H. Fessler and L. I. Fessler, *Proc. Natl. Acad. Sci. U.S.*, **56**, 141 (1966).
23. T. C. Laurent, *Biochim. Biophys. Acta*, **136**, 199 (1967).
24. B. Öbrink, *J. Chromatog.*, **37**, 329 (1968).
25. E. F. Casassa, *J. Am. Chem. Soc.* **78**, 3980 (1956).
26. J. S. Fawcett and C. J. O. R. Morris, *Separation Sci.*, **1**, 9 (1966).
27. M. Partridge, *Biochim. Biophys. Acta,* **140**, 132 (1967).
28. G. K. Ackers, *Biochemistry*, **3**, 723 (1964).
29. E. M. Renkin, *J. Gen. Physiol.*, **38**, 225 (1955).
30. J. N. Brønsted, *Z. Physik. Chem. Bodenstein Festband,* **1931**, p. 257.
31. P. Å. Albertsson, *Partition of Cell Particles and Macromolecules,* Wiley, New York, 1960, p. 100.
32. J. C. Moore and J. G. Hendrickson, *J. Polymer Sci. C*, **8**, 233 (1965).
33. B. Öbrink, T. C. Laurent, and R. Rigler, *J. Chromatog.*, **31**, 48 (1967).
34. K. Selby and C. C. Maitland, *Biochem. J.*, **94**, 578 (1965).
35. N. V. B. Marsden, *Ann. N.Y. Acad. Sci.*, **125**, 428 (1965).
36. B. Z. Ginzburg and D. Cohen, *Trans. Faraday Soc.*, **60**, 185 (1964).
37. A. G. Ogston, *Arch. Biochem. Biophys. Suppl.* **1**, 39 (1962).
38. H. Hint, *Symposium on Rheomacrodex,* London and Cardiff, 1964, Vol. 1, Pharmacia international, Uppsala, p. 2.
39. T. C. Laurent and A. G. Ogston, *Biochem. J.*, **89**, 249 (1963).
40. T. C. Laurent and E. P. Laurent, *J. Chromatog.*, **16**, 89 (1964).
41. J. C. Giddings and K. L. Mallik, *Anal. Chem.*, **38**, 997 (1966).
42. T. C. Laurent, in *The Chemical Physiology of Mucopolysaccharides,* G. Quintarelli, Ed., Little, Brown, Boston, Mass., 1967, p. 153.
43. B. S. Blumberg and A. G. Ogston, *Biochem. J.*, **63**, 715 (1956).
44. A. G. Ogston and C. F. Phelps, *Biochem. J.*, **78**, 827 (1961).
45. T. C. Laurent, *Biochem. J.*, **89**, 253 (1963).
46. T. C. Laurent, *Acta Chem. Scand.*, **17**, 2664 (1963).
47. B. R. Gerber and M. Schubert, *Biopolymers*, **2**, 259 (1964).
48. B. N. Preston, M. Davies, and A. G. Ogston, *Biochem. J.*, **96**, 449 (1965).
49. K. Hellsing, *Acta Chem. Scand.*, **19**, 1791 (1965).
50. K. Hellsing, *J. Chromatog.* **36**, 170 (1968).
51. A. G. Ogston and B. N. Preston, *J. Biol. Chem.*, **241**, 17 (1966).
52. W. F. Dudman, *Biochim. Biophys. Acta,* **120**, 212 (1966).
53. W. F. Dudman, *Nature,* **211**, 1049 (1966).
54. K. A. Granath and B. E. Kvist, *J. Chromatog.*, **28**, 69 (1967).
55. Å. Wasteson, *Biochim. Biophys. Acta,* In press.
56. T. C. Laurent and K. A. Granath, *Biochim. Biophys. Acta,* **136**, 191 (1967).
57. Th. Wieland, P. Duesberg, and H. Determann, *Biochem. Z.*, **337**, 303 (1963).

58. J. R. Whitaker, *Anal. Chem.*, **35,** 1950 (1963).
59. P. Andrews, *Biochem. J.*, **91,** 222 (1964).
60. P. Andrews, *Biochem. J.*, **96,** 595 (1965).
61. D. M. W. Andersson and J. F. Stoddart, *Anal. Chim. Acta,* **34,** 401 (1966).
62. T. I. Pristoupil, *J. Chromatog.*, **19,** 64 (1965).
63. J. J. Cebra and P. A. Small, Jr., *Biochemistry,* **6,** 503 (1967).
64. Z. Grubisic, P. Rempp, and H. Benoit, *J. Polymer Sci.*, **5,** 753 (1967).
65. L. W. Nichol, J. L. Bethune, G. Kegeles, and E. L. Hess, in *The Proteins,* Vol. II, H. Neurath, Ed., Academic Press, New York, 1964, p. 305.
66. D. J. Winzor and H. A. Scheraga, *Biochemistry,* **2,** 1263 (1963).
67. D. J. Winzor and L. W. Nichol, *Biochim. Biophys. Acta,* **104,** 1 (1965).
68. G. A. Gilbert, *Anal. Chim. Acta,* **38,** 275 (1967).
69. G. K. Ackers, *J. Biol. Chem.*, **242,** 3026 (1967).

Separations Based on Size and Conformation *

LYMAN C. CRAIG, HAO-CHIA CHEN, AND ELIZABETH J. HARFENIST

The Rockefeller University, New York, New York

The other papers of this volume present much material showing the importance of diffusional size as a separation parameter for the isolation and characterization of large molecules and organized particles. This attention is not overemphasized and I shall try to emphasize it further by discussing mainly our studies with membrane diffusion. This approach obviously bears a close similarity to gel filtration as regards certain basic aspects which, however, will not be discussed because of the material presented by Laurent and Joustra (see their chapters in this volume). From the standpoint of true understanding "thin film dialysis" is a singularly simple and uncomplicated separation procedure. It is clearly a rate process capable of surprisingly high selectivity. The particular properties of molecules it is capable of revealing may well be of great importance in many other separation procedures.

Apart from the practical use of dialysis one cannot escape the fact that a cellular structure is characteristic of living things and that regulation of concentration gradients as well as many enzymatic reactions involve or depend on the close proximity of membranes. Nature has apparently found membrane diffusion and membrane phenomena to be among the best basic parameters for the extremely selective separations often required. The realization of this fact has stimulated such an enormous research effort and resultant literature as to make the field almost completely confusing. It is obvious that the processes are complicated and delicately balanced, and even yet only partially understood. Irrespective of this state of affairs little can be found in the massive literature which will be helpful in improving the applicability and selectivity of simple dialysis as a separation tool. One may well ask what new approach now might be exploited.

* The studies reported in this paper were supported in part by a grant, No. A-2493, from the National Institutes of Health.

About ten years ago it occurred to us that due to the nature of our work we were accumulating a wide variety of cyclic peptides, alkaloids, sugars, proteins, etc. carefully documented as to structure, size, shape, solubility, etc. and that by dialysis studies these might be used as models to learn something about the properties of membranes pertinent to separation, perhaps about the pore structure of semipermeable membranes, if indeed there is a true pore structure. Thus began the approach that will be discussed here.

Some thirty-five years ago, before the ultracentrifuge was developed, ultrafiltration was a popular approach for determination of the molecular size of proteins, viruses, etc. It was observed that at a critical size just below total rejection there appeared to be a rapid increase in the selectivity and a theory was proposed by Elford (1) and Ferry (2) to account for the observation. This theory, illustrated schematically in Figure 1, was considered to apply equally well to dialysis. The equation, where A is the available cross sectional area of the pore, r is the diameter of the particle and R that of the pore, gives the change in free space available for diffusion as the size of the particle approaches that of the cross section of the pore. The frictional drag on the pore walls then becomes a main factor in determining the selectivity. This drag may be expressed in terms of a frictional coefficient or "reflection coefficient," a term proposed by Staverman (3) in his equations dealing with osmotic pressure phenomena in leaky membranes. These theories have been refined mathematically much beyond that given here and perhaps beyond experimental justification but the simplest form without doubt is useful in understanding the nature of the effect.

In attempting practical improvements in dialysis, previous experience indicates numerous difficulties. It is a slow process, thought to be due in part to quiescent liquid film resistance on both sides of the membrane; there are charge effects either to be overcome or exploited; the membrane becomes clogged or adsorbs the solute, etc. These objections probably cannot be 100% eliminated but by the proper choice of apparatus, solvent, solute concentration, controls, etc. they can be minimized to the point of becoming at least second-order effects.

In tissues the overall physical arrangement provides an enormous

$$A = A_0 (1 - r/R)^2$$

Fig. 1. A schematic concept of membrane selectivity.

membrane surface exposed to very shallow solution depths. Thus all the solution is well within the quiescent so-called "Nernst" layer. In addition, the membranes are in continuous movement and under a certain pressure due to osmotic effects. Some of these conditions are partially met in the experimental analytical dialysis cell shown in Figure 2. Details of this simple arrangement will not be discussed here since they are well described in the literature (4,5). The rate of dialysis is determined by inserting a solution of known concentration inside the membrane (retentate) and following the decrease in concentration by periodic replacement and analysis of the diffusate solution. The process can be considered to have a relationship to osmotic

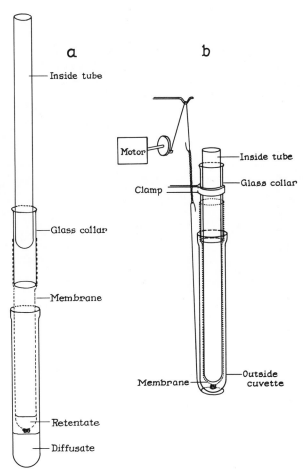

Fig. 2. Schematic drawing of an analytical thin film dialysis cell.

pressure studies in leaky membranes, in that instead of following the decrease of concentration by the fall of osmotic pressure the rate of escape through the membrane is directly determined. A much wider choice of conditions and membranes can be studied thereby than with osmometry.

Results are expressed as a semilog plot of concentration fall against time. An ideal pure solute should give a straight line as shown in Figure 3a, if the concentration gradient across the membrane is the only driving force. The necessary conditions to achieve this have been extensively investigated with Visking Cellophane tubing. It has been possible to achieve adherence to a straight line to a rather surprising degree.

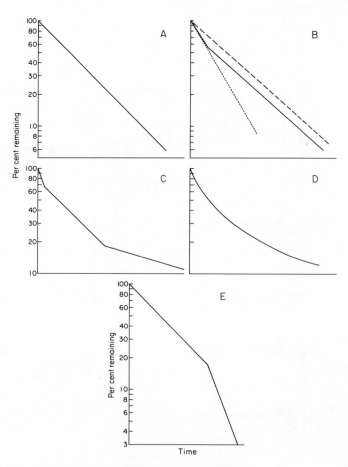

Fig. 3. Types of escape plots.

With this point established it was possible to explore the behavior of mixtures and solutes showing nonideal behavior. A mixture of two different sizes of ideal solutes will give two rates whose sum will be the intermediate curve shown in Figure 3b depending on the relative amounts. A mixture of three solutes could give the result shown in Figure 3c while a more complex mixture could give that shown in Figure 3d. Solutes known to aggregate often give a negative deviation as shown in Figure 3e.

Obviously the significance of such escape patterns is a function of the selectivity of the membrane. As discussed earlier, it has been shown that selectivity is a function of pore size in the critical range near the total exclusion point. It therefore becomes important to be able to adjust at will the pore size (as reflected by escape rate) for any desired solute. We have published simple procedures for accomplishing this with cellophane by mechanical stretching, by acetylation to reduce pore size, and by $ZnCl_2$ treatment to increase pore size. The ranges include those suitable for studying molecular weights from 100 to 100,000.

A more concrete idea of the selectivity offered can be obtained by considering data we have accumulated with model solutes. Table I (6) gives a comparison of the relative half-escape times of certain sugars with relative diffusion coefficients taken from the data of Longsworth (7). The increased selectivity due to the membrane resistance is obvious. However, it should be understood that the membrane measurements provide only relative estimates, not physical constants.

Perhaps a more concrete estimate of the selectivity possible can be given by a study of the cycloamyloses (6). Here the ring structure of the hexamer whose dimensions are accurately known from X-ray diffraction studies, differs from the heptamer by a diameter increase of about 11%. The discrimination obtained with a membrane of suitable pore size is shown in Figure 4. One can estimate from this chart that with careful work a difference in diffusional diameter of 2–3% should be recognizable. By way of comparison, gel diffusion is generally considered to reflect differences in diffusional size. It certainly is one of the most useful separation techniques in biochemistry but is not free of adsorption effects and in our hands has not shown the selectivity demonstrated in Table I and in Figure 4.

This brings up the question of adsorption, its recognition and minimization. Adsorption on the membrane can be recognized easily by simple recovery experiments (8). It may cause a deviation from straight line behavior and interestingly enough, if of the right degree and type, may considerably accelerate diffusion. Adsorption effects

TABLE I

Comparison of Relative Diffusion Rates with Half-Escape Times

Substance	MW	D × 10⁶	D ratios	½ ET (hr)	½ ET ratios
Xylose	150	7.462		1.3	
			— 1.02		1.46
Arabinose	150	7.599		1.9	
			1.13		1.84
Glucose	180	6.728		3.5	
			1.01		1.37
Galactose	180	6.655		4.8	
			1.28		6.2
Sucrose	342	5.209		30	
				1.5	
			1.03		1.73
Lactose	342	5.076		2.6	
			1.01		1.04
Cellobiose	342	5.039		2.7	
			1.16		2.0
Raffinose	504	4.339		5.4	
			1.13		2.8
Stachyose	666	3.839		15	
				0.68	
			1.19		1.64
Cycloheptaamylose	1152	3.224		1.1	
Cyclohexaamylose	972	3.443		6	
			1.07		2
Cycloheptaamylose	1152	3.224		12	
			1.07		1.91
Cyclooctaamylose	1296	3.000		23	

may be minimized by addition of dissociating components to the solvent system; acetic acid, formamide, methanol, etc. Adsorption effects tend to increase as the solute size approaches total exclusion. This in fact can well be a large part of the basis for the size separation of gel filtration. Adsorption effects are known to be more noticeable with Sephadex G 10 and with Biogel p-4 than with the more porous gels.

As regards charge effects, these can be separated into two categories; the fixed charge on the membrane and the distribution of charges on the diffusing molecule. Visking Cellophane has been shown to be as nearly free of fixed charge as could be expected (8). Our many published experiments with charged solutes have shown that the rate of diffusion bears no relationship to isoelectric point or sign of charge for those solutes which have rigid conformations. On the other hand, with

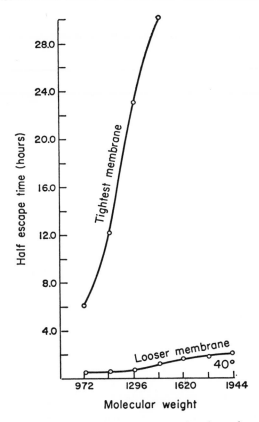

Fig. 4. Plots of relative escape rates of cycloamyloses.

linear peptides or proteins which have a degree of conformational flexibility, a marked decrease in escape rate has been noted upon addition of salt to the solvent when the charges are of opposite sign and located some distance apart on the chain (9). For example, in Table II the half-escape time of peptide Tβ12 is not influenced while the others are. In contrast to such behavior is that of charged solutes with charges of only like sign distributed along the chain. Here the shielding effect of the salt decreases the mutually repelling effect of like charge and allows the molecule to assume a more compact form. The polynucleotides show a marked increase in escape rate when salt is added. With them mg^{2+} ion seems to have a specific effect in accelerating dialysis.

It would appear obvious that a diffusion technique with the size selectivity thus far demonstrated would be highly sensitive to con-

TABLE II

T/2 of Hemoglobin Peptides

Peptide [a]	No. of A.A.	0.01M HOAc pH 3.3, hr	0.2M NH₄OAc 0.3 M HOAc pH 4.46, hr	0.15M NH₄OAc 0.01M HOAc pH 5.8, hr
Tα9	7	1.8	—	4.9
Tβ12	10	6	5.7	4.8
Tβ4	12	3.8	8.5	7.8
Tβ1	13	5.1	17	12.8
Tα12	15	7.4	—	—
Tα12	15	2.5 [b]	6 [b]	—

```
                     +  −                        +  −
Tα9 :  Val-Asp-Pro-Val-Asp(NH₂)-Phe-Lys
        +                                              +
Tβ12:  Leu-Leu-Val-Val-Tyr-Pro-Tyr Thr-Glu(NH₂)-Arg
        +  −                                                +  −
Tβ4 :  Glu-Phe-Thr-Pro-Pro-Val-Glu(NH₂)-Ala-Ala-Tyr-Glu(NH₂)-Lys
        +              −   −                  −            +  −
Tβ1 :  Val-Asp(NH₂)-Val-Asp-Glu-Val-Gly-Gly-Glu-Ala-Leu-Gly-Arg
        +        +       −          −            −  +  −
Tα12:  Val-Gly-Ala-His-Ala-Gly-Glu-Tyr-Gly-Ala-Glu-Ala-Leu-Glu-Arg
```

[a] Peptide designations
[b] In more porous 18/32 membrane.

formation and also to aggregation. The published data leave little doubt that this is true (5). Temperature and denaturation studies with urea, formamide, alcohol, etc. have been much as would be expected. Where there is aggregation as in the case of tyrocidine (10), urea, formamide, alcohol, etc. increases the escape rate from that shown for tyrocidine in Figure 5 to that for gramicidin S which does not associate or to tyrocidine with the ring split. On the other hand, these agents slow it markedly with deformable peptides such as ACTH (11) (figure 6). These conclusions have been supported by studies with the ultracentrifuge where there has been uncertainty arising from aggregation.

Attempts to support our dialysis conformation studies by rotatory dispersion results have emphasized the difficulty of interpreting rotatory dispersion data in terms of conformation. Thus tyrocidine B and gramicidin S (12) both gave dispersion curves (Figure 7) of the type widely ascribed heretofore to the helical conformation. Because of their ring structure neither of these can be helical. In 50% methanol the rotatory dispersion curve of tyrocidin B was unchanged but thin film dialysis indicated complete dissociation. From the dialysis data

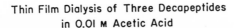

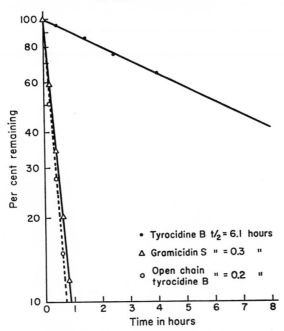

Fig. 5. Escape plots of three peptides.

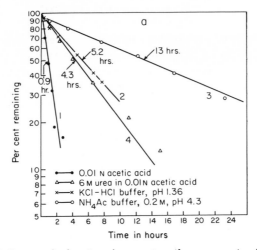

Fig. 6. Influence of solvent environment on the escape rate of ACTH.

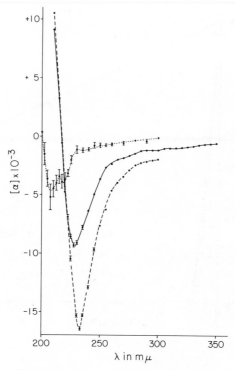

Figure 7. Rotatory dispersion curves: (—) tyrocidine B; (—.—) gracimidin S; (. . .) tyrocidine B with the ring split.

in Table II it can be seen that a conformational shift is indicated with the first peptide on addition of ammonium acetate. A change in the rotatory dispersion curve was also noted. This, however, was in contrast to the behavior with ACTH (Figure 6) where the rotatory dispersion curve was not shifted by ammonium acetate. These data show that while rotatory dispersion data may indicate the presence of a certain type of conformation or conformational change the type and extent of molecular involvement is entirely uncertain at the present time. Bacitracin, another type of cyclic polypeptide antibiotic has also given a rotatory dispersion curve with a deep minimum at about 233 mμ. Others have not shown such behavior.

If a wide variety of solutes added to the solvent can appreciably change the conformation of a large polymeric molecule in solution it seems important to ask how this is brought about. Do they interfere with hydration, charge interaction, bind specifically, or act otherwise? The question of binding would seem especially pertinent to explore. Strong binding is easy to recognize by a variety of techniques including dialysis. Thus the half-escape time of actinomycin B in thin film dialysis is more than doubled by an equimolar amount of 5'-deoxy-guanylic acid, a known specific binding agent (13) only a fraction the size of actinomycin B.

Weak binding, however, is not so easily recognizable. Recently a much more sensitive dialysis technique has been suggested. It came about through attempts to devise an efficient continuous countercurrent dialyzer for preparative purposes (14). Only a brief description of the important features of this apparatus will be given. A schematic drawing is given in Figure 8.

The device is an attempt to achieve a controlled uniform flow in opposite directions of two thin solution films which are separated by a semipermeable membrane. This is accomplished in an annular space

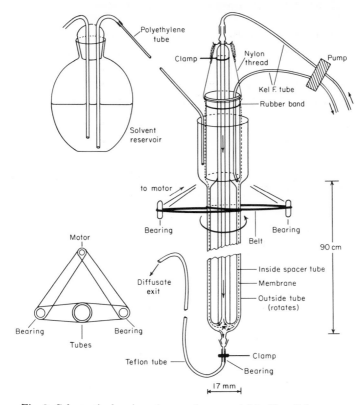

Fig. 8. Schematic drawing of a countercurrent thin film dialyzer.

0.3 mm in depth between concentric glass tubes approximately 90 cm in length. The membrane area presented is approximately 500 cm². The two streams are controlled by small pumps with minimal holdup volumes and connected to the apparatus with capillary (No. 22) Kel-F tubing. The retentate stream is introduced through a capillary in the center of the inner concentric glass tube inside the Visking tubing which is tied off at the bottom of the inner tube. It then rises as a film inside the membrane to the top where it is pumped out to a fraction collector. The diffusate stream enters at the top outside the membrane but inside the outer tube and flows downward in a film past the membrane, out the bottom and also into a fraction collector. Spinning the outer tube prevents channeling, provides efficient stirring and a gentle massage of the membrane.

A 1-ml pulse of a solution containing 1N NaCl and dextran blue, introduced in the retentate stream, will give the effluent patterns shown in Figure 9 for retentate and diffusate streams. All the detectable salt will be in the diffusate stream. The apparatus was developed to give the sharpest patterns possible in this type of test.

A better estimate of the efficiency can be derived by means of tritiated water. Here a pulse containing 10^8 counts/min introduced in the retentate stream can be essentially reduced to background on the scintillation counter in a single pass. Thus with a residence time of 6–8 min the concentration of tritium will be reduced at least six orders of mag-

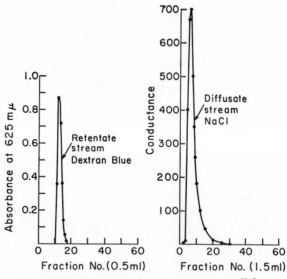

Fig. 9. Effluent patterns from countercurrent dialyzer.

nitude and transferred to a diffusate flow about threefold that of the retentate. Such rapid exchange obviously suggests many applications for the study of tritium exchange, binding studies, desalting operations, size separations, etc. It can be thus a useful tool to extend and support the information derived from earlier static thin film technique.

Lysozyme is now a highly characterized protein and therefore a good model with which to test new techniques. When incubated with tritiated water for a given time and then passed through the dialyzer the retentate stream will be cleared of free tritium as shown in Figure 10 where the curves of absorbance at 280 mμ and the counts/min in the scintillation counter exactly coincide. The number of bound tritiums can be calculated easily from such data.

The salt effect on proteins can now be investigated further. It has been found that lysozyme and other proteins seem to undergo a change in diffusional size with a change in ionic strength of the solution as shown in Figure 11. Dr. Chen in my laboratory obtained these data. The half-escape times of the three proteins all seem to show a maximum change at ionic strengths between 0.001 and 0.1. Dr. Chen then in-

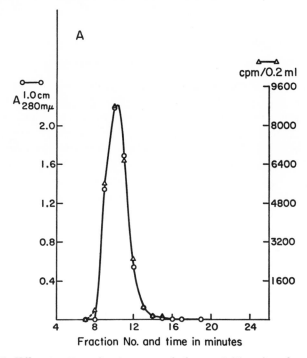

Fig. 10. Effluent pattern showing removal of excess tritium from lysozyme.

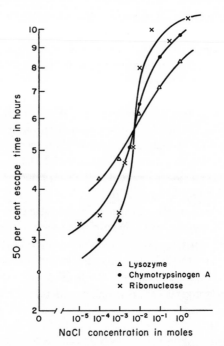

Fig. 11. Effect of salt on the escape rate of lysozyme, ribonuclease, and chymo-
trypsinogen.

vestigated the tritium exchange rates of lysozyme at different ionic
strengths as shown in Figure 12. Both exchange in and out were found
to be different for low ionic strength as compared to high. A change
in conformation is therefore indicated by this technique since sodium
chloride would not be expected to influence proton exchange rates in
the absence of a conformational change.

Dr. Chen has also studied the binding of N-acetyl glucosamine
(NAG) by the countercurrent dialysis technique. In Figure 13, he used
as solvent a solution with a known counts/min of radioactive NAG.
Pulses of different concentrations of lysozyme were then introduced
successively. The effluent retentate stream was monitored by absorbance at 280 mμ as shown. Counts from the scintillation counter were
then plotted after subtracting the counts/min of the solvent. The
variations are due to errors in counting and are apparently exaggerated
since they are difference results after subtracting the much larger
counts/min of the solvent. The limit of error in counting is of the order
of a few percent. The advantage offered here is that many points can
be determined quickly and the results plotted statistically as shown in

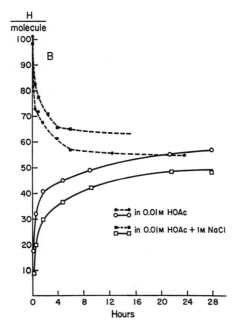

Fig. 12. Tritium exchange rates with lysozyme.

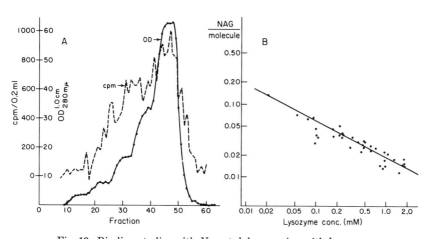

Fig. 13. Binding studies with *N*-acetylglucosamine with lysozyme.

the right-hand chart of Figure 13. The weak binding constants found are of the same order as those published by Rupley and co-workers (15) but a definite drift with increasing concentration of lysozyme was noted.

The diffusional size parameter is likely to be much more important in the separation of large molecules than is commonly realized. The tRNA mixture is of special interest in this connection. It happens to be a mixture of 50 or more polynucleotides each of molecular weight approximating 30,000. Countercurrent distribution (16) gave the first separation approaching purity of a single member of the group and has been widely used as has partition chromatography. In the Goldstein system (17) a spread of partition ratios extending from 0.3 for alanine tRNA to 7 for tyrosine tRNA can be obtained. It seems pertinent to ask why large solutes of this similarity show such striking differences in partition ratio. The answer to this most probably lies in the differences in conformational change that each tRNA undergoes in passing from the aqueous-rich phase to the alcohol-rich phase on each partition. There is considerable evidence for conformational change in these nucleotides particularly from the work of Khym (18), Henley et al. (19), and others. One also cannot neglect the probability of interaction with each other since the distributions usually are nonideal. The components of all the systems which have shown promise are those known to have detergent properties or to interact strongly with large molecules.

Dr. Harfenist and Dr. Chen have tried to exploit the Goldstein system by more extensive CCD and have achieved the overall separation shown in Figure 14 using CDCD for initial group separation and subsequent 2000 T CCD of each initial cut from the CDCD. *Escherichia coli* tRNA was used in this work. It is obvious that a large starting sample must be used for so many components and when all the required assays have been made with the desired precision a large part of each individual tRNA would be used up. The continuous countercurrent dialyzer can be important in removing salts, formamide, etc. from the system and also promises to afford a more sensitive assay procedure. This aspect is presently under development.

Dr. O'Neal of Rockefeller University suggested that in the bioassay after incorporation of the radioactive amino acid into the tRNA the excess unbound radioactive amino acid be removed by the thin film dialyzer instead of by precipitation of the amino acyl tRNA with TCA. He and Dr. Chen achieved the result shown in Figure 15, assaying this way for leucine sRNA in a sample of crude mixed *E. coli* tRNA. The successive bands are revealed by plotting the results of the counts/min

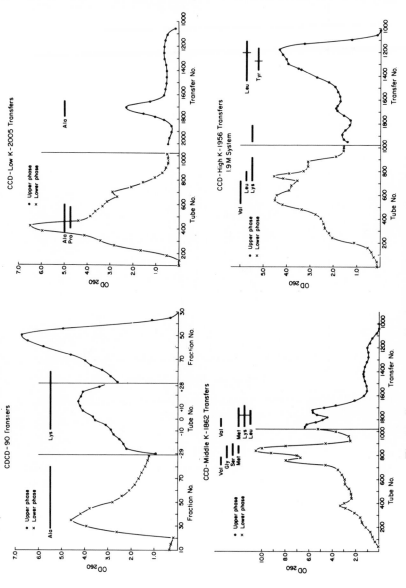

Fig. 14. Countercurrent distribution patterns with *E. coli* tRNA.

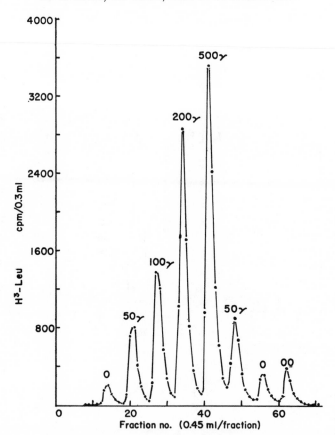

Fig. 15. Retentate plots following successive injections of various amounts of tRNA in incorporation mixtures.

and amounts of sRNA. Thus band 1 arises from 50 μg of tRNA, band 2 from 100 μg, band 3 from 200, etc. Figure 16 is a plot of sample weight against the integrated band counts/min. Since a 50-μg sample of this mixed tRNA contains only about 2 μg of leucine tRNA it would appear that the method can be of considerable significance in sRNA fractionation. The limits for all the amino acid tRNA's have not been determined as yet.

In this brief review we have tried to show by the use of membrane diffusion that the parameter of diffusional size can be employed in such a way that it alone not only provides a very selective basis for separation, but at the same time can give much information about the molecule. This information can be very helpful in planning separation

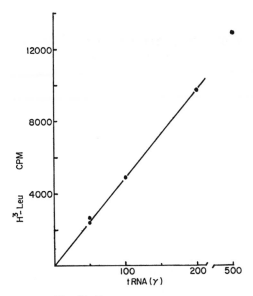

Fig. 16. Dose response curves.

procedures and may take some of the empiricism out of the choice of methods and specific conditions.

References

1. W. J. Elford, *Proc. Roy. Soc. (London), Ser. B*, **105**, 216 (1930) ; *Trans. Faraday Soc.*, **33**, 1094 (1937).
2. J. D. Ferry, *J. Gen. Physiol.*, **20**, 95 (1936).
3. A. J. Staverman, *Trans. Faraday Soc.*, **48**, 176 (1948).
4. L. C. Craig and W. Konigsberg, *J. Phys. Chem.*, **65**, 166 (1961).
5. L. C. Craig, in *Methods of Enzymology*, Vol. XI, C.H.W. Hirs, Ed., Academic Press, New York, 1967, p. 870.
6. L. C. Craig and A. O. Pulley, *Biochemistry*, **1**, 89 (1962).
7. L. G. Longsworth, in *American Institute of Physics Handbook*, D. E. Gray, Ed., McGraw-Hill, New York, 1957, p. 193.
8. L. C. Craig and A. Ansevin, *Biochemistry*, **2**, 1268 (1963).
9. L. C. Craig, *Science*, **144**, 1093 (1964).
10. M. A. Ruttenberg, T. P. King, and L. C. Craig, *Biochemistry*, **5**, 2857 (1966).
11. L. C. Craig, J. D. Fisher, and T. P. King, *Biochemistry*, **4**, 311 (1965).
12. M. A. Ruttenberg, T. P. King, and L. C. Craig, *J. Am. Chem. Soc.*, **37**, 4196 (1965).
13. E. Reich, *Science*, **143**, 684 (1964).
14. L. C. Craig and K. Stewart, *Biochemistry*, **4**, 2712 (1965).
15. J. A. Rupley, L. Butler, M. Gerring, F. J. Hartdegen, and R. Pecoraro, *Proc. Natl. Acad. Sci. U.S.*, **57**, 1088 (1967).
16. J. Agpar, R. W. Holley, and S. H. Merrill, *J. Biol. Chem.*, **237**, 796 (1962).

17. J. Goldstein, T. P. Bennett, and L. C. Craig, *Proc. Natl. Acad. Sci. U.S.*, **51**, 119 (1964).
18. J. X. Khym, *J. Biol. Chem.*, **241**, 4529 (1966).
19. D. D. Henley, T. Lindahl, and J. R. Fresco, *Proc. Natl. Acad. Sci. U.S.*, **55**, 191 (1966).

Author Index

Numbers in parentheses are reference numbers and show that an author's work is referred to although his name is not mentioned in the text. Numbers in *italics* indicate the pages on which the full references appear.

240 AUTHOR INDEX

Davies, M., 212, *217*
Davis, B. J., 1, 2, *21, 22*
Denson, K. W. E., 51(11), *68*
Determann, H., 183, *197*, 200, 215(57), *216, 217*
Dike, G. W. F., 51(11), *68*
Doty, P., 113(3), *119*, 160(19), *166*
Dougherty, T. F., 178(10), *181*
Dudman, W. F., 212, *217*
Duesberg, P., 215(57), *217*
Durrum, E. L., 47(6), *68*

Eberhagen, D., 51, *68*
Edgell, M. H., 1, 17(4,13), *21, 22*
Ekman, R., 80(17), *90*
Elford, W. J., 220, *237*
Eylar, E. H., 131(71), *145*

Falaschi, A., 112(22), *119*
Favre, J,. 113(23), *119*, 150(4), 155(4), 159(4), 161(4), 164(4), *165*
Fawcett, J. S., 204, *217*
Ferry, J. D., 220, *237*
Fessler, J. H., 203, *217*
Fessler, L. I., 203, *217*
Field, C. W., 183, *198*
Fischer, L., 200(9), 206, 210, *216*
Fisher, J. D., 226(11), *237*
Flodin, P., 200, 201(12), *216, 217*
François, C. J., 57, *69*
Fresco, J. R., 234(19), *238*
Friberg, U., 81(18), *90*
Frick, G., 113(29), *119*, 153(10), *166*
Fridborg, K., 195, *198*
Friedman, H., 47, *68*
Fröhlich, Ch., 50, 51(9), *68*
Fuji, T., 54(17), 55(17), *68*
Fulwyler, M. J., 99(1), *102*

Ganser, M., 61(30), *69*
Garvin, J. E., 91, *102*
Garza, R., 109(38), *120*, 121(3,5,8), 123(5), 124(5), 130(5), 131–133(5), 136, 137(8), 140(22), 141(5,20), *145*
Gelotte, B., 183, *197*, 200(8), *216*
Gerber, B. R., 212, *217*
Gerring, M., 234(15), *237*
Giddings, J. C., 210(41), *217*
Gilbert, G. A., 216(68), *218*

Ginzburg, B. Z., 208, *217*
Glimcher, M. J., 57, *69*
Goldstein, J., 234, *237*
Granath, K., 183, 188, *197*, 214, 215, *217*
Grant, C. T., 113(24), *119*
Grassmann, W., 47(1,4), 55(18), *68*
Grubisic, Z., 215, *218*
Gürtner, T., 56, *69*

Hannig, K., 45, 47(1,4,5), 48, 50, 52 (13), 58(28), 59(29), 60(29), 61(30, 13), 62(31,32), 63(31), 64(32), 65(32, 33), 66(33,35), *68, 69*
Harfenist, E. J., 219, 234
Harington, J. S., 87(24,26), *90*
Harley, J. D., 87(25), *90*
Hartdegen, F. J., 234(15), *237*
Haskill, J. S., 94(5), 101(5), *103*, 167(2, 3), *181*
Haydon, D. A., 130(16), *145*
Hayek, D. H., 72, *90*
Heller, G., 65(34), *69*
Hellsing, K., 199, 212, 213, 216, *217*
Hendrickson, J. G., 207, 214(32), *217*
Henley, D. D., 234, *238*
Hershey, A., 154(14), 164(14), *166*
Hess, E. L., 216(65), *218*
Hilal, S. K., 170(7), *181*
Hint, H., 209, *217*
Hippel, P. H. v., 192(17), *198*
Hjertén, S., 1(3), *21*, 183(6), 184, 195 (19), *197, 198*, 200(4), *216*
Hobom, G., 58, *69*
Höglund, S., 72(8), 82(8), 88(8), *90*, 195(19), *198*
Hörmann, H., 54(17), 55(17), *68*
Hoffman, P., 57, *69*
Hohn, Th., 201(14), 202, *217*
Holdsworth, E. S., 47(4), *68*
Holley, R. W., 234(16), *237*
Howze, G. B., 79(16), *90*
Hutchison, C. A., III, 1, 17(4,12,13), *21, 22*
Hvidt, A., 171, 172, *181*

Iler, R. K., 72, 87(7), *90*
Inman, R., 153(12), *166*

Subject Index